VETERINARY HOSPITAL MANAGEMENT

Third Edition of the
Veterinary Hospital Manual

Waltham USA, Inc.
P.O. Box 58853
Vernon, California 90058
Phone: 1-800-528-1838
Fax: 1-213-586-8363
Internet: www.waltham.com (user ID: waltham; password: nutrition)
Email: drwaltham@aol.com

Printed in U.S.A.

Designed and published by Veterinary Learning Systems, a division of MediMedia

ISBN 1-884254-40-3

To the veterinary hospital staff

*For their crucial role in promoting
the health and well-being of
their patients and their practice*

CONTENTS

1 HOSPITAL APPEARANCE

1 The Reception Room
2 The Laboratory
2 Examination Rooms
2 Rest Rooms
3 Decorating Tips
6 Removing Stains
12 Eliminating Odors

13 OFFICE COMMUNICATIONS

13 Scheduling Appointments
14 Handling Delays
14 Clients Without an Appointment
15 Other Visitors
15 Client Checkout
16 Referral Letters
16 Business Letters
16 Newsletters and Brochures
18 The Hospital Policy Manual
19 Staff Vacancies

25 TELEPHONE COMMUNICATIONS

25 Telephone Courtesy
28 Follow-up Calls
28 Long Distance Calling
30 Answering Machines

31 FILING AND RECORDKEEPING

32 Computer vs. Paper Systems
33 Filing Systems
36 Storage Options
36 Receipts
38 Directory of Vendors and Suppliers
39 Medical Recordkeeping
41 Identification Systems for Hospitalized Animals
46 Common Abbreviations

53 EQUIPMENT AND SUPPLIES

53 Office Equipment
60 Medical Equipment
60 Equipment Malfunction and Repair
61 Purchasing and Storing Office Supplies

64 MAIL ROOM PROCEDURES

64 Receiving Packages and Mail
64 Shipping Parcels
65 Diagnostic Specimens
66 Postal/Courier Services

76 CLIENT/PROFESSIONAL RELATIONS

76 Effective Communication
77 Medical Instructions and Compliance
78 Problem Encounters
83 Professional Liability (Malpractice)
86 Sexual Harassment
87 Substance Abuse

89 PERSONAL MANAGEMENT

89 Time Management
90 Coping With Stress
93 Projecting a Professional Image

95 HOSPITAL SAFETY AND SECURITY

95 Creating a Safety Program
99 If You Are Injured on the Job
99 If a Client Is Injured at the Veterinary Hospital
99 Building Security

102 HUMAN EMERGENCIES AND FIRST AID

102 Calling for Help
102 Fainting and Unresponsiveness
104 Animal Bite Wounds
105 Life-Threatening Emergencies
105 Courses in First Aid and CPR
108 The First Aid Kit

109 DRUG GUIDELINES

109 Dispensing Prescription Drugs
110 Extralabel Drug Use
110 DEA Guidelines

113 REGULATORY AGENCIES

113 U.S. Department of Agriculture (USDA)
114 U.S. Department of Health and Human Services
115 U.S. Department of Justice
115 Environmental Protection Agency (EPA)
115 Association of American Feed Control Officials (AAFCO)

117 TRAVELING WITH PETS

117 Traveling by Car
118 Traveling by Airplane
119 The Health Certificate
119 Travel to Another State
119 Travel to a Foreign Country

121 CANINE CARE

121 CANINE Data Chart
121 Bathing
123 Reproduction
125 Puppy Care
127 Preventive Health Schedule
129 Dental Care
131 Surgery
133 Vaccinations
134 Parasites
139 Behavior Problems
141 Diet and Feeding

145 FELINE CARE

145 FELINE Data Chart
145 Bathing
146 Reproduction
147 Kitten Care
149 Litter Training
150 Dental Care
151 Surgery
153 Vaccinations
155 Parasites
156 Behavior Problems
157 Diet and Feeding

161 EQUINE CARE

161 EQUINE Data Chart
162 Housing
162 Dental Care

163   Vaccinations
163   Parasites
165   Trimming and Shoeing
166   Lameness
166   Colic
166   Behavior Problems
167   Diet and Feeding

169   FOOD ANIMAL CARE

169   CATTLE Data Chart
170   Management Goals
171   Reproduction
172   Injections
172   Calf Care
172   Diet and Feeding
174   SWINE Data Chart
176   CAPRINE Data Chart
177   OVINE Data Chart
178   OSTRICH Data Chart
179   RHEA Data Chart

181   AVIAN CARE

181   BUDGERIGAR Data Chart
182   PARROT Data Chart
183   CANARY Data Chart
184   COCKATIEL Data Chart
185   MACAW Data Chart
186   COCKATOO Data Chart
187   FINCH Data Chart
188   PIGEON AND DOVE Data Chart
188   MYNAH Data Chart
189   Orphan Birds

193   OTHER EXOTIC ANIMALS

193   FRESHWATER AND MARINE FISH Data Chart
194   SNAKE Data Chart
196   LIZARD Data Chart
197   TURTLE Data Chart
198   GERBIL Data Chart
199   GUINEA PIG Data Chart
200   HAMSTER Data Chart
201   RABBIT Data Chart
202   FERRET Data Chart

HOSPITAL APPEARANCE

The professionalism and character of a veterinary practice are reflected by the setting. A dark, dingy, dirty-looking environment makes a totally different impression on a client than an open, airy, immaculate facility. Clients should feel that they are bringing their pets to a clean, safe, efficient place.

In many cases the staff has a lot of input in the setup and upkeep of a veterinary clinic, and frequently this aspect of management is almost exclusively the veterinary technician's responsibility. If major changes in the clinic are required, especially structural changes, an expert such as an architect or planning consultant will be needed. If all the clinic needs is a little decorating, you can undertake the task yourself. If it's within the budget, hiring a decorator for advice on flooring, wall covering, and window treatments is helpful.

THE RECEPTION ROOM

Visitors form their first main impressions of a veterinary hospital in the reception area, which should be inviting and comfortable. Spaciousness and light are key elements to making the room pleasant. If your area is neither of these, keep the primary decorating colors on the light side, avoid dark paneling, and hang light, airy curtains in the windows.

Ideally, the waiting area should be divided in half to separate clients with dogs from those with cats. A low wall, aquarium, large planter, or counter can serve as the room divider.

Most new veterinary hospitals are designed with built-in benches in the reception area. These are a good idea, as they simplify cleaning, and pet leashes cannot become entangled in them as they can in chairs. Wooden benches can be quite attractive.

A U-shaped reception counter provides an efficient area for both receptionist and client. It is helpful to have a private area to the side for discussing bills and payments.

1

The materials and structures throughout the veterinary hospital should be durable and easily cleaned. For walls there are a variety of choices, including washable paint, vinyl flooring that extends partway up the wall, tile, or a laminated plastic wainscot. Ceramic tile is a good covering for floors, as it can withstand abuse from harsh disinfectants and animals' nails. Other durable floorings include vinyl tile and sheet vinyl.

A reception room feature that can be a real plus is an attractively done display case for veterinary products and pamphlets. Displays add interest to the waiting area, are informative for clients, and generate another source of revenue for the practice. The maintenance required to keep display cases neat is worth the extra effort.

THE LABORATORY

To maximize efficiency, there should be easy access between examination rooms and the laboratory. Walkways between these areas should be spacious to accommodate heavy traffic. A laboratory sink can be used after an examination if the rooms are in close proximity.

Sufficient space should be allotted for each piece of laboratory equipment as well as for performing diagnostic tests. An uncluttered area for these tasks is essential.

EXAMINATION ROOMS

Examination rooms should be uncluttered and large enough to comfortably accommodate both client and pet. They should be cleaned after each visit. A spotless, stainless-steel examination table is the focus of the examination room. Chairs should be provided for the client and veterinarian; these can be wall mounted or free standing and should be kept well off to the side.

Textured vinyl or one of the materials mentioned previously can be used on the walls. Plastic laminate counters and a central vacuuming system facilitate cleaning.

Soundproofing is a special consideration in examination rooms. Walls should not be hollow, acoustic tile ceilings are advisable, and doors should be insulated.

REST ROOMS

It is best to have separate rest rooms for employees and the public.

These areas, like all others in the veterinary hospital, should be regularly cleaned throughout the day. Care should be taken to amply stock toilet paper, soap, and towels.

DECORATING TIPS
Colors

Choosing colors is one of the most important decorating decisions, for they are important in creating the atmosphere you would like. A feeling of friendly welcome in a reception area can be achieved with colors such as cream, yellow, rose, and green. A sunny room with southern exposure can be beautifully decorated in blue, brown, black, gray, and burgundy, but such colors should be avoided in darker rooms.

Once you have decided on the color scheme, try to carry these colors throughout the office. While flooring should be uniform throughout the hospital, each individual room may have different types of wall-covering and curtaining, with care taken that colors flow between one room and another.

When you plan the color scheme, pin swatches of the different fabrics, wallpaper or wallcovering, and pieces of paper covered with the paints you will use to one large sheet of paper. You will find this a more efficient and objective way of balancing tones and contrasting colors rather than relying on your memory.

Greater decorating success will generally be achieved if colors of floors, curtains, and wallcoverings are kept as subdued and neutral as possible. This does not mean that curtains and wallcoverings should not have any patterns or designs. It simply means that the effect should be quiet rather than startling. Bold motifs may look spectacular at first, but the effect may soon become tiring. Peaceful colors also aid in better concentration and greater harmony among coworkers. Keep the contrast as slight as possible between the larger items. Splashes of color can then be introduced in many ways such as colorful paintings, potted plants, or a vase of fresh flowers. All of these should echo or complement the basic color used on the walls and curtains.

Lighting

Natural lighting is always best, as it reduces eye and mental fatigue and provides a more relaxing atmosphere than bright electric lighting. An airy feeling may also help keep the animals calm. Window treatments should allow in as much light as possible. If a room is dark, skylights can be added or small windows enlarged.

Of the various types of electric lighting, fluorescent provides the softest, best-diffused light for the office. Ceiling lighting also eliminates the need for standing or table lamps, which can accidentally be knocked over.

Plants

Healthy, beautiful greenery can go a long way to enhancing the look of the veterinary hospital. The choice of plants for your particular conditions is important. Any good garden center or nursery can advise you on selection. The brighter the light level inside the practice, the greater the choice of plants. Even for clinics with fairly low light levels, there are many good options that can add some life to the surroundings. Be sure that any plants you choose are either nontoxic or are hung high out of reach of your patients.

Plant Care Tips
Watering

Don't drown your plants. Most plants do better when given a good watering occasionally as opposed to being watered a little every day. Indoors, particularly with air conditioning, you will find it necessary to water only once a week (or even every 2 weeks for certain plants). A good way to know when to water is to plunge your finger into the compost to the full depth of your fingernail. If your fingertip remains dry, the plant needs watering. Alternatively, you can use a moisture meter (a very simple gauge available at garden centers).

Always check the saucers under the plants after watering to ensure that your plants are not standing in water. If they are, remove the excess.

Lighting

Make sure the lighting is appropriate for the plant. If a plant is not thriving, it might do better in a location with more or less light.

PLANT SUGGESTIONS FOR THE CLINIC

Low Lighting
♦ *Dracaena*—Comes in a range of shapes and sizes and is available in plain or variegated forms.
♦ *Chamaedora elegans*—A dark green and lush miniature palm that is very suitable for fairly dimly lit areas and needs very little attention
♦ *Algaonema*—Leaf colors include plain green, silver, and variegated yellow

Taller Plants
♦ Bamboo palm—Soft and graceful; multistemmed
♦ *Ficus benjamina*—Loses many of its leaves when moved; once settled, however, it thrives easily

Other Recommendations
♦ *Aspidistra elator*—Called the cast iron plant because of its ability to withstand practically any conditions
♦ *Chlorophytum comosum*—Spider plant
♦ *Dizygotheca elegantissima*—Excellent for a lacy contrast to larger leafed plants
♦ *Fatshedera lizei*—Ivy tree
♦ *Ficus elastica decora*—Rubber tree
♦ *Cissus antartica*—The kangaroo vine, a trailing plant that is almost indestructible

"Throw-Away" Plants (long-lasting but need to be replaced from time to time)
♦ Chrysanthemums
♦ Cyclamen
♦ African violets—Can flower off and on for years if grown in a very bright but not sunny spot

Feeding

Feeding plants is very easy. There are a great variety of products on the market (e.g., liquid foods, pills, and plant sticks or stakes) that come with full instructions.

The plant stick is probably the easiest of these for the busy clinic. These fertilizer sticks are staked in the soil, into which they slowly release fertilizer for up to 6 weeks. The number of sticks depends on the particular size pot you are using.

It is an excellent idea to spray plants occasionally, especially during their growing season, with foliar food. Buy a small hand sprayer and, about once a month, spray plants with one of the organic leaf foods available.

Cleaning

Sponge lightly using only clean water; young leaves should not be washed. Other easy cleaning methods are to place plants outside for a few hours when it's raining or use a hand-held shower head to spray plants put in a tub.

Aerosols and wipe-on liquids available for polishing leaves can clog the plant's pores. If you must use these products, do so only occasionally.

REMOVING STAINS

Despite the best upkeep possible, any veterinary hospital will incur its share of stains on everything from employees' clothing to floors and furniture. Keep a stain removal kit on hand as quick removal is often the secret to preventing permanent stains. Whenever possible, use commercial stain removers that are designed to eliminate specific stains.

Some of the items in the kit must be accompanied by a label that includes safety information as required by OSHA and state law (see p. 95). When using stain removal substances, wear appropriate protective gear, including gloves, mask, and goggles.

The basic technique for stain removal is as follows:

♦ If the stain is **dry** or **glutinous,** scrape it off with a dull knife or any thin-edged tool.
♦ If it is still **wet,** absorb it. Touch the tip of a white paper tissue, towel, sponge, absorbent cotton, or white cloth into the stain without applying any pressure that would push the stain into the material. Sprinkle an absorbent powder on grease stains.
♦ If the liquid has **soaked in,** there are several alternatives.
　—For water-based stains on washable materials, flood the area with cool water.
　—For nonwashable fabrics (1) sprinkle an absorbent powder on the stain or (2) for nongreasy stains put a clean, dry absorbent pad under the stain, use an eyedropper to apply cool water, and blot immediately with another clean absorbent pad or tis-

THE COMPLETE STAIN KIT

♦ White paper tissues/towels/white cloth handkerchiefs
♦ Dull knife for scraping off residue
♦ Small tube of commercially prepared absorbent material (dry stick or paste form)
♦ Small can of dry-cleaning spray
♦ Sponge
♦ Eyedropper
♦ Cotton swabs
♦ Toothbrush
♦ Eraser
♦ Sandpaper (fine) or emery cloth
♦ Laundry presoak products, including an enzyme soak
♦ Common dry-cleaning fluid
♦ Ammonia
♦ Liquid detergent
♦ Borax or other washing soda
♦ Vinegar (white)
♦ Rubbing alcohol
♦ Hydrogen peroxide
♦ Bleach (nonchlorine and chlorine)

sue on top. Repeat until the stain can no longer be transferred to the pads.

—Absorbents should be pretested on a hidden seam or hem. After pretesting, sprinkle on the powder or apply the paste and let the first application stand a few minutes. Then turn the cloth over and shake or brush it off. The second time you might have to brush or push the absorbent into the fabric with a dull knife; let it stand again, and finally brush it off.

♦ If a spot has **dried,** spot a lubricant or solvent soak on it for at least 20 minutes or up to several hours before trying to lift the soil. The liquid must be confined to a small area and kept moist. Reapplying the solvent sparingly with an eyedropper at intervals will work better than flooding the fabric, which will cause solvent rings. You can also place moistened pads with solvent both above and below the spot and cover with an inverted bowl to help keep them from drying out.

♦ Some solvents evaporate completely and leave no residue. Oth-

---

STAIN REMOVAL TIPS

♦ **Speed is essential.** About 90% of most food and beverage, greasy and nongreasy spots will come off with either ordinary dry cleaning fluid or detergent and water if they are attacked while the substance is wet and/or still on the surface of the fabric. This grace period varies with the absorbency of the cloth and the repellency of its finish. The stain undergoes chemical changes that set the stain permanently when exposed to sunlight and/or heat, as time passes, and as it penetrates the material.

♦ **Less is more.** The way you apply a solvent can either spread the stain and grind it into the fabric or lift it out. Use as little suds or fluids as possible. The best way to prevent rings is to use a solvent-moistened pad to lightly dab from the center of the spot toward its edges. Blot dry remaining fluid by sandwiching the sponged area between dry absorbent pads. Don't use heat if you used liquids other than water.

♦ **Check the labels.** Use a product made specially for stain removal, if possible. Take appropriate precautions (e.g., put on mask and/or gloves) per the label instructions. Also, check the label of the stain-causing substance for instructions on removing stains.

♦ **Test for colorfastness.** Place a white tissue or white cotton cloth under the fabric and drip an eyedropper filled with the solvent onto it. Gently wipe a cotton swab or white tissue over the area once or twice in one direction, then turn the cleaning tip and wipe in another direction. Look to see whether either the pad underneath or the cotton swab has any dye on it.

♦ **Watch the spot.** Don't leave a garment unattended after applying solvent or laundry presoak if you have never removed that kind of stain on that fabric before. Cleaning aids such as enzyme presoaks may be safe for a few minutes but can deteriorate the dye if left on longer.

---

ers must be removed to prevent deterioration of the cloth. For nonwashables, place a clean, dry absorbent pad under the solvent-wetted area and add small amounts of water or dry cleaning fluid. Pour or drip no faster than the pad can soak it up to keep the wetted area as small as possible and to prevent rings.

If you have done everything you can and are still left with a mark, it may be possible to lighten the spot or even erase it with a mild bleaching agent without harming the surrounding area:

♦ Before bleaching, remove any remaining grease or oil with a dry-cleaning fluid or, if the fabric is washable, with a laundry presoak and washing.

STAIN REMOVAL NO-NOs

♦ **NEVER** apply water to oil-based inks, paints, lipstick, and other grease stains, which may release dyes or set the stain. Water and rubbing can also permanently flatten acetate velvet pile.

♦ **NEVER** apply dry cleaning fluid to clothes labeled "do not dry clean."

♦ **NEVER** use water and dry cleaning fluid together. Remove the greasy stain first, dry the material, and then work on the water-soluble part of the spot.

♦ **NEVER** subject stained material to heat, hot water, or ironing.

♦ **NEVER** apply milk or salt to stains (contrary to popular belief).

♦ Wet the area with a small amount of water before applying the bleach so there won't be a demarcation line around the spot.

♦ Pretest the bleaching agent on a seam.

♦ Apply the bleaching agent.

—The first alternative is to apply a solution of one part hydrogen peroxide and an equal amount of water, using a cotton swab for small spots or an eyedropper for larger ones. Put an absorbent pad underneath the area to prevent the liquid from spreading.

—Lemon juice is another mild bleach you can try.

—If you need a stronger solution, try diluting an oxygen bleach (such as Clorox 2) with lots of water. Avoid the strong chlorine bleaches because they will remove all color.

♦ Once the stain has been removed, neutralize the agent to stop the bleaching. Lemon juice can be neutralized with diluted ammonia, and alkaline bleaches (i.e., most commercial bleaching products) can be neutralized with lemon juice. Then flush the area with water, using an eyedropper if the fabric cannot withstand large amounts of liquid.

Special Cases

♦ **Blood**—Flush area with hydrogen peroxide, and then soak in cold water. **Always wear gloves** when cleaning up blood.

♦ **Laboratory dyes**—Stains used for microbiologic specimens may spill on countertops or in sinks. Rubbing alcohol will usually remove these stains.

♦ **Urine**—A wide variety of products are available for removal of animal urine and its odor. First blot up as much moisture as possible with an absorbent cloth. Apply odor neutralizer and let it set according to label instructions. Older stains may need several applications to significantly reduce the odor.

♦ **Vomit and Feces**—Vomit has strong stomach acids that can be neutralized with ammonia and water. Rinse and follow with an enzyme presoak product that you mix into a paste. This is also effective on feces. When vomit is fresh, use spray-on foam carpet shampoo on upholstery after sponging with the presoak. Over time, vomit causes irreversible damage to any natural fiber because of its high acidity.

♦ **Chewing gum**—Harden the spot with cold air and scrape it when the chilled gum becomes brittle. If the stained item is small, put it in a plastic bag and leave it in the freezer for about an hour. If the garment is large, rub the gum with an ice cube encased in plastic.

♦ **Cigarette burns**—For light scorches use a commercial presoak that contains glycerin. Cover the lubricant with an inverted bowl to keep it moist and let stand overnight, if necessary. Then sponge with water and detergent and rinse. Heavy scorches may be impossible to remove.

♦ **Grass**—If the stain is light and recent, many presoak and heavy duty detergents may take care of it. If it is ground in and/or it has set, sponge with dry cleaning fluid and dry. An absorbent paste with acetone may also work.

♦ **Ink**—If the spot is wet or damp, apply an absorbent first. Because there are many different kinds of formulas for ink, you may need to try several solvents.

—If you suspect water-soluble ink, apply a laundry presoak product. Use clean absorbent pads above and below the spot and change as the ink transfers to the pads. Flush or sponge with water and repeat several times, if necessary.

—If you believe the ink is a dye (found in many ballpoint pens), it may respond to rubbing alcohol or denatured alcohol. Dilute the alcohol with two parts water for rayon. A commercial ink remover is available at many stationery and art supply stores.

VETERINARY HOSPITAL DISINFECTION SCHEDULE

Areas Requiring Disinfection	Recommended Frequency	Areas Requiring Disinfection	Recommended Frequency
Examination rooms		*Ward*	
Counters	Twice daily	Cages	Twice daily
Sinks	Twice daily	Runs	Twice daily
Tables	After each use	Eating and drinking	Daily
Floors	Daily	utensils	
Walls	Weekly		
		X-ray rooms	
		Counters	Daily
Treatment rooms		Equipment (aprons,	Daily
Counters	Twice daily	gloves)	
Sinks	Twice daily	Tables	After each use
Tables	After each use	Floors	Weekly
Floors	Daily	Walls	Weekly
Walls	Weekly		
		Reception areas	
Surgery		Seating	Daily
Counters	Twice daily	Windowsills	Daily
Sinks	Twice daily	Restrooms	Daily
Tables	After each use	Floors	Daily
Floors	Daily	Walls	Weekly
Walls	Weekly	Sidewalks and	Daily
		walkways	
Pharmacy		Carpeting	As needed
Counters	Daily		
Floors	Daily		
Walls	Weekly		

— If the stain remains, it may have a resin base. Apply acetone and flush it out with dry cleaning fluid for nonwashables or with water for washables.

— Alternatively, stubborn stains may have a petroleum base. Sponge with dry-cleaning fluid or turpentine. Petroleum jelly may soften and lubricate the spot so that you can lift it with dry-cleaning fluid.

— If all else fails, try bleaching.

♦ **Mildew**—Mildew is removed with different types of products, depending on the type of stain.

— Light mildew can be destroyed with a strong detergent. For garments, launder and hang them to dry in sunlight. If the cloth is colorfast, try spot washing or sponging with one part hydrogen peroxide to four parts water and then rinse well. For white materials you can use stronger bleaching solutions or an oxygen bleach.

—For heavy stains on fabric, start by sponging with dry cleaning fluid. Work gently because the mold may have weakened the fibers. If a stain still remains and the fabric is washable, try a laundry presoak product that contains glycerin. Let stand, launder, and dry.

—If the stain remains, sponge with alcohol. If alcohol should not be used on the fabric, take it to a dry cleaner.

ELIMINATING ODORS

Odor control is a significant issue in the veterinary hospital. A good ventilation system is a must. High ceilings help tremendously, as do vents or exhaust fans in the ceiling.

Minimize the number of places where urine can collect. Baseboards should be eliminated and replaced with floor covers extending up to the wallcovering. Rooms should be uncluttered and contain as little furniture as necessary to facilitate cleaning.

Disinfection is a key practice in any veterinary hospital. You should have an effective disinfection program planned that you adhere to faithfully. A schedule designed to provide adequate disinfection for the average veterinary hospital is shown on p. 11.

Disinfectants have several properties. The detergent in the product aids in removal of any residual organic matter that remains after the preliminary cleaning. The deodorant destroys odor-producing bacteria before they can interact with organic matter. Some products are also virucidal (i.e., they destroy or inactivate viruses) and/or fungicidal.

Different disinfectants are suitable for different tasks, so care must be taken in selecting the proper one. In applying a disinfectant, prepare and use it exactly as directed, and observe the safety precautions for handling concentrates.

Bibliography

Jones M: *Taking Care of Clothes*. New York, St. Martin's Press, 1982.

OFFICE COMMUNICATIONS

SCHEDULING APPOINTMENTS

Appointments are usually made by telephone. Often this is the very first contact between staff and client. For this reason rules about telephone etiquette (see p. 25) are important.

Scheduling can be a complicated matter. It is important to allot sufficient time to provide the care and counseling needed for each appointment, but you don't want to waste time between patients.

Some basic guidelines to keep schedules running smoothly follow:

♦ Determine the hospital policy about length of office visits. In some clinics the length varies depending on the service provided (e.g., complete examinations may require more time than routine vaccinations). In others a specified time—perhaps 20 minutes—is allotted for every case.

♦ Do not overburden the staff. Do not schedule more appointments than can be supported by the number of doctors, the number of examination rooms, and the length of the schedule day.

♦ Tell clients the times and dates of available appointments and let them choose. Do not ask open-ended questions (e.g., "When would you like to see the doctor?") as these often elicit suggestions that do not fit the practice schedule.

♦ Information you must obtain from the client when scheduling an appointment includes:
  —The client's name and telephone number
  —The pet's name and species
  —The purpose of the visit

♦ Make sure the client understands any special instructions concerning the visit (e.g., for yearly checkups, remind client to bring a stool sample).

♦ Confirm appointments a few days in advance, unless the

appointment was made less than 2 weeks previously. Some clinics routinely call all clients the day before their appointment as a reminder.

♦ Keep appointments light on days before and after long weekends and holidays.

♦ Consider allotting a portion of the schedule (e.g., 10 to 15 minutes/hour) to emergency visits.

The receptionist should have a list of appointments for each day. When a client or other caller with an appointment arrives, the veterinarian or other appropriate staff member should be notified immediately unless he or she is busy and cannot be interrupted. It is best to announce the caller so that you can discuss any delay or special considerations with the veterinarian (e.g., the veterinarian may prefer to see the caller in his or her office rather than in an examination room). Accompany the client to the examining room as soon as it is ready.

HANDLING DELAYS

If someone with an appointment must be kept waiting, apologize, and explain the delay ("Dr. Grant has had an emergency, but she will be free in a few minutes. Will you have a seat?"). Telling the client approximately how long the delay will last gives him or her the opportunity to decide whether to wait or reschedule the appointment. If you know in advance of their arrival that clients will not be seen within 15 minutes of the appointed time, you should attempt to notify them before they come in.

CLIENTS WITHOUT AN APPOINTMENT

When clients bring their pets to the clinic without an appointment, ask whether the problem is an emergency or if it can wait until an appointment can be scheduled. Only in cases of emergency should the schedule be rearranged.

If the animal's condition is not a medical emergency, explain to the client that the schedule is fully booked and that you regret not being able to accommodate the visit immediately. Schedule an appointment for the first available opening. Last minute cancellations and unused emergency slots can sometimes be used to schedule the appointment for the same day or the next.

Some clinics allow a client without an appointment to drop off a pet so that the veterinarian can examine the animal later in the day. If yours has that policy, be sure you get a phone number where the client can be reached. Clearly explain the procedures that will be performed on the animal (usually just an examination), and state that no other procedures will be performed unless the doctor can reach the client for approval. Explain the costs, including any daily hospitalization fee.

OTHER VISITORS

When you know that the veterinarian is not interested in seeing or is too busy to see someone who is not a client, you might say: "I wish I could be more helpful, but Dr. Evans' schedule is fully booked for the next week. We are having an unusually busy time. May I suggest that you call the doctor at a later time or, if the matter isn't urgent, write him?" You may be able to suggest a time for placing the call that suits the veterinarian's schedule.

In many cases someone else on staff will be able to help. If the visitor has sales material or samples to distribute, offer to take the samples and show them to the appropriate person at an opportune time.

CLIENT CHECKOUT
Discharging Patients

When possible, schedule a specific time for clients to pick up their animals. This allows the staff to ensure that the animal is clean and its medications are ready to go when the client arrives. Either the doctor or a technician should be available to discuss home care with the client.

Collecting Payment

A printed estimate should be given to all clients for all but the most simple procedures. New clients, even if visiting for only a physical examination and vaccinations, should be told of the charges to expect before they see the doctor.

At the time the estimate is given, ask clients how they intend to pay the bill ("Will you be paying by check, cash, or credit card?"). With the estimate in hand and a discussion of how they plan to pay, there should be no problems with payment when clients are ready to leave.

REFERRAL LETTERS

The referral letter is an important document. With accurate, comprehensive information pertaining to a patient's history, another veterinarian can make appropriate choices regarding future care without wasting time and money or missing pertinent information that has already been obtained. All details of the patient's history that could affect the animal's current condition or treatment should be given:

♦ State the presenting complaint.
♦ List tests performed and their outcomes.
♦ Describe treatments and the patient's progress.
♦ Explain why the referral is being made.
♦ List any secondary or general conditions (e.g., a heart problem or kidney disorder) that may affect the treatment or prognosis.
♦ Note any special diet, medication (give specific drug names, as well as the dose and course of treatment), or other treatment that the animal is currently receiving.

BUSINESS LETTERS

A business letter or memo should convey information simply, clearly, and concisely. While a flair for writing is an advantage, it is not necessary. Everyone can write effective business letters by following a few basic rules:

♦ Understand the overall purpose of your letter.
♦ Get all the facts together.
  —Carefully read any letter you may be answering and underscore the main points in colored pen or pencil.
  —If you are initiating the correspondence rather than replying, list all the information that you want to obtain or convey.
♦ Prepare an outline. Make sure the correspondence will cover who, what, when, where, why, and how.
♦ Whenever possible, personalize your letters.

NEWSLETTERS AND BROCHURES

Many hospitals provide an informational brochure for new clients and a newsletter for existing clients. Both types of publications are

HOW TO SET UP BUSINESS LETTERS

Style (any of the following are acceptable)
♦ **Semiblocked style**—The date and complimentary close are placed at the middle of the page and each paragraph is indented five spaces.
♦ **Blocked style**—Similar to semiblocked except the paragraphs are not indented.
♦ **Full-blocked style**—All parts are placed flush with the left margin.

Margins
♦ **Right and left margins**—Make at least 1 inch wide. If the letter is short, the width of each side margin can be 2 inches or more.
♦ **Bottom margin**—Make at least 1½ times that of the side margins.

Spacing
♦ Single-spacing is recommended for business letters.
♦ Insert one line of space between paragraphs, between the address and salutation, and between the salutation and the first line of the message.
♦ Insert two lines of space between the last line of the letter and the complimentary close.
♦ Leave four lines of space between the date and the address at the top, as well as for the signature at the bottom.

Heading
♦ Place the date at the top of the letter
♦ Next, place the addressee's full name and address

Salutation
♦ Whenever possible, use an individual's name in the salutation.
♦ Use "Dr." for physicians or veterinarians. For other individuals use "Mr." for men and "Ms." for women unless you know that they prefer "Miss" or "Mrs."
♦ Use a colon following the salutation (e.g., "Dear Mr. Smith:").

Complimentary Close
♦ Personal phrases include "Sincerely," "Cordially," "Sincerely yours," "Cordially yours," and "Very sincerely yours." Formal phrases include "Yours very truly," "Very truly yours," and "Respectfully yours."
♦ Use a comma after the complimentary close.
♦ Below the sender's signature, his or her full name and degree(s) (if applicable) should appear on one line followed by his or her title on the next.

DESIGN TIPS FOR NEWSLETTERS/BROCHURES

♦ Break up copy with heads, boxed information, lists, etc. These elements should be used to point up the most important information for the reader.

♦ Use art and other graphic elements where appropriate to make the piece more inviting to the reader.

♦ There are many different typefaces, but only two basic kinds: serif type, which has short lines that extend beyond the stroke of a letter itself, and sans serif type, which does not.
—This is an example of a serif typeface.
—This is an example of a sans serif typeface.

♦ In general, long passages of copy are easier to read in serif type.

♦ Don't use too many typefaces (more than two or three) throughout a publication.

---

effective tools for communicating with the public and educating them about your practice.

It is vital that a newsletter or brochure reflect an impeccable professional image. Staff members who are very proficient at writing, typesetting, and layout may be able to prepare brochures and newsletters on a computer, which are then professionally printed. Some clinics may decide that the staff's time and effort are better spent elsewhere, however, and will hire outside help to produce these materials.

Newsletters may be written and produced in-house, by an outside firm, or by one or more staff members with assistance from an outside professional. There are also companies that mass produce prewritten newsletters that can be personalized with your hospital's name.

Brochures range from simple text-only to elaborate full-color pieces with photographs. The brochure should contain basic information such as the name/address/phone number (including an emergency phone number, if available) of the hospital, hours open, a list of the staff, and services available. A simple brochure can be designed with the help of a good book from the library. Professional help should be enlisted for a more elaborate brochure (e.g., hire a professional photographer to take any pictures you want to include).

THE HOSPITAL POLICY MANUAL

Every hospital should have a policy manual to ensure that all staff members understand how the hospital is to be run and what is expected of them. Sections in the manual should include:

- ♦ Hospital polices (everything from extending credit to clients to vaccination protocols)
- ♦ Hiring policies and interviewing techniques (see next section)
- ♦ Job descriptions (details for every job)
- ♦ Employee evaluation criteria
- ♦ Hospital safety manual (see p. 95)
- ♦ Sexual harassment policy (see p. 86)

Information about how to write a hospital policy manual is available from the AAHA, in journals such as *Veterinary Economics,* and in books.

STAFF VACANCIES
Permanent Positions

Veterinary technicians are often required to find prospective junior employees for the practice. This is an important responsibility. The individual selected to fill a staff vacancy should be one who will grow and develop as an asset to the practice, will be happy in the position, and will be compatible with clients as well as other staff members.

Job Descriptions

Before a staff vacancy is advertised or listed with an employment agency, compile a comprehensive job description to establish the responsibilities of the job and the background and experience required

---

JOB DESCRIPTIONS: ESSENTIAL COMPONENTS

- ♦ Title
- ♦ Department
- ♦ Hours
- ♦ Purpose or overall job objective
- ♦ Duties
- ♦ Reporting relationships
- ♦ Cooperative relationships
- ♦ Working conditions (physical and social)
- ♦ Salary range
- ♦ Prospects for promotion
- ♦ "Ideal candidate" (experience, intelligence, aptitude, interests, attitude, goals)

CLASSIFIED AD CHECKLIST

❑ Job title (receptionist, veterinary technician, etc.)
❑ Qualifications needed
❑ Experience necessary
❑ Nature of your company (i.e., veterinary practice)
❑ Special qualities required (e.g., "an outgoing personality")
❑ Future prospects (e.g., training or promotion)
❑ Salary*
❑ Telephone number and name of person whom candidates should call or address to which resumes should be sent. (If applicable, specify "No calls, please.")

---

*Whether or not to include the salary level is decided by your employer. If it is not, a statement indicating that the figure is "negotiable" or "competitive" can be helpful.

---

or preferred. A job description is particularly important if job responsibilities have changed since the position was last filled or if a new position has been created.

Placing an Advertisement

An advertisement in the local newspaper and/or a professional journal (e.g., *Veterinary Technician*) is often the best way to seek employees. Writing an effective advertisement that includes all the necessary information is extremely important in reaching the best prospective employees.

The advertisement should be eye catching. It may be worthwhile to pay extra for bigger and bolder type.

Aim at making the position sound inviting, but don't mislead job hunters with improbable promises or deceptive statements.

Job Interviews

Once candidates for the job have been selected, study the facts available about them (e.g., test results, application forms, resumes, and educational certificates) prior to the interview. Note any time gaps or inconsistencies on application forms and resumes that should be probed during the interview. To ensure quiet and privacy, make arrangements to avoid interruptions and telephone calls during the meeting.

It is up to you, the interviewer, to put applicants at ease. By winning their confidence at the start, you will make the interviews more productive in terms of obtaining accurate information and impressions about the individuals.

Ensure that the receptionist is expecting each applicant and knows his or her name. Upon meeting the applicant, greet him or her by name and introduce yourself.

Your opening remarks should create an atmosphere of two-way communication. Small talk can help the interviewee relax before you move into the actual interview phase.

The purpose of the interview is to obtain as much information as possible about the candidate that is relevant to the position, particularly how well his or her skills match those needed. Make sure you allow enough time to conduct the interview properly. Prepare a list of questions to follow during each interview. Standard questions include:

♦ What is your work history?
♦ What did you like/dislike about your last job?
♦ What are your strengths/weaknesses?
♦ Why would you like to work here?
♦ Where would you like to be in 5 years?

INTERVIEW DOs AND DON'Ts

Don't Ask About...
♦ Marital status
♦ Birthplace
♦ Age
♦ Religion
♦ Disabilities
♦ How/When citizenship was obtained
♦ Nonprofessional affiliations
♦ Applicant's/Spouse's maiden name
♦ Relatives/Relatives' jobs
♦ Criminal record
♦ Children/Pregnancy/Family plans
♦ Physical size/weight
♦ Bond refusals
♦ Possessions (owning a home/car)

Do Ask About...
♦ Ability to work certain hours or days
♦ Ability to work overtime
♦ Ability to perform specific tasks required for the job, such as any of the following:
—Clerical skills
—Ability to lift certain amounts of weight
—Computer savvy

At the conclusion of the interview, tell candidates when they will hear the result of their application or what the next step in the process will be. (This is an opportunity to find out if they have applied for or been offered any other job.)

A Nine-Point Plan for Successful Interviews

♦ Set applicants at ease with a friendly, open manner.

♦ Take note of applicants' dress and overall appearance to see if they conform to the standards of your practice.

♦ Ask open-ended questions that will encourage applicants to talk. You should do about only 20% of the talking during the interview.

♦ Remain in control of the interview and redirect applicants when digressions occur.

♦ Be interested and sincere and keep to a logical line of questioning. Jumping from topic to topic will confuse applicants, especially those who are applying for a job for the first time.

♦ Take notes, but only enough to jog your memory.

♦ Make sure that the interview takes place in a relatively private environment without interruptions or telephone calls.

♦ Be very clear about the new employee's area of responsibility and the kind of attitude necessary for the practice atmosphere.

♦ Outline what the new employee will learn in the position and whether there is room for advancement. Also highlight any training offered.

Interpretation and Evaluation

Evaluate the candidate while the details are fresh in your mind. If you haven't taken notes during the interview, do so immediately after.

Be objective in your evaluations. The candidates' qualifications are the most important criteria, but projection of a professional image (through dress, speech, and body language) should be a factor as well.

Always call the references of the finalists. Ask open-ended questions about the applicants' strengths and weaknesses. Remember that previous employers may not be as candid as you'd like because of concerns about potential legal repercussions. Ask questions that have a factual answer, such as "Was this person on time for work?" One revealing question you may ask is "Would you hire this person again?" You may also ask applicants' references for the names of additional persons with whom the applicant has worked and call them.

Employment Agencies

You may find it practical to use the services of an employment agency. Screening and selecting candidates for a job is a time-consuming process, and it may be worthwhile to pay the agency's fee rather than evaluate a long list of candidates yourself. In selecting an agency, consult other veterinary professionals who may have used such services in the past and ask for their recommendations. Also be sure you understand the agency's terms and how they compare with those of other agencies.

When you contact the agency, give exact details of the skills required and the work expected, as well as the standards of performance. Describe the working environment as well as the people with whom the new staff member will be working.

If the agency provides full-time permanent staff, payment of wages is made directly to the person employed and a one-time commission is paid to the agency. If, for a valid reason, your practice finds the employee unsatisfactory, the commission is usually refundable within a stated time (e.g., 90 days). These are only general guidelines. Clarify all such points with the agency before agreeing to accept its services.

Legal Considerations

To avoid legal problems, you should become familiar with the laws

---

TEMPORARY HELP

When temporary help is needed, an agency can usually fill the demand quickly. Temporary staff furnished by a good agency are generally experienced and can adapt to new situations easily.

For temporary help, you may be required to give assurance that you will not attempt to hire workers that the agency has recruited for you without paying a commission. Such clauses usually specify a period (e.g., 6 months) between the initial work period of the individual and the direct hiring. Payment is made to the agency, not the person employed, consisting of wages plus a commission for the agency.

enforced by the Equal Employment Opportunity Commission (EEOC). These laws state that you may not discriminate against an applicant on the basis of the applicant's race, religion, sex, national origin, or age. Employers are prohibited from paying lower wages to employees of one sex who perform equal work on a job requiring the same level of skill, effort, and responsibility and under similar working conditions, except where payment is based on a seniority or merit system. Laws prohibit age discrimination against individuals between the ages of 40 and 64.

The Americans with Disabilities Act (ADA) prohibits discrimination based on disabilities. ADA requires reasonable accommodation for applicants and workers with disabilities when such accommodations would not impose "undue hardship."

Make sure that your interview and your application form concern matters that affect actual job performance. Some information that would be discriminatory when requested from a job applicant may be asked for insurance purposes after the applicant has already been hired. That information may not be used to discriminate in promotion or work assignment decisions.

TELEPHONE
COMMUNICATIONS

TELEPHONE COURTESY

The first contact almost every one of your clients has with your clinic is made by telephone. Courtesy and efficiency in answering and placing calls are key to a thriving practice. Staff members responsible for answering incoming phone calls should have a pleasant manner as well as a positive and helpful attitude.

Most experienced veterinary personnel are already skilled in telephone diplomacy, but some pointers may be helpful for new staff members:

General Notes

♦ Answer promptly (within three rings). If for some reason the phone rings several times before you are able to answer it, apologize for the delay.

♦ Smile before you pick up the telephone, which can help give you a friendly tone and manner.

♦ Announce the name of the clinic and follow with "May I help you?" Never answer with a simple "Hello."

♦ Keep a message pad or telephone log notebook by the telephone. ALWAYS write messages down. Note the caller's name (ask the client to spell it, if necessary), telephone number, and the time and date of the call. Sign the message with your initials.

♦ If you must make a personal call at work, do not do so when you are in the reception area or visible to clients. This can give a less than businesslike impression to clients.

What to Say

♦ Always use the caller's name. It conveys the feeling that you consider this person important.

♦ Use titles and surnames, when appropriate (e.g., always refer to veterinarians and physicians as "Dr. _____").
♦ For other individuals use the client's surname (e.g., Mr. Smith) unless you are on a first name basis with the individual. (Always ask if you can refer to clients by their first name before you begin doing so.) Use "Ms." (pronounced "Miz") to address a woman rather than Mrs. or Miss, unless you know the caller's preference.
♦ Avoid using technical terms or abbreviations, which are probably unfamiliar to the caller.
♦ Common courtesies such as "please" and "thank you" can help convey a friendly manner to clients.

Putting Callers on Hold
♦ Use your hold button only when absolutely necessary.
♦ Always ask permission to put someone on hold.
♦ Never put someone on hold for more than 30 seconds.
♦ If after 30 seconds you still cannot direct your attention to the call, return to the caller, apologize for the delay, and determine whether the call is an emergency.
♦ If the situation is not an emergency, ask if you can call the client back in a few minutes. Take the client's name and number, and repeat it back for verification.
♦ Make sure you return the call promptly as promised!

Juggling Callers and Visitors
♦ When doing double duty answering calls and greeting clients, always acknowledge visitors with a nod or wave and eye contact.
♦ If you anticipate that the phone call will take more than a minute or two, you can either:
   —Ask if you can return the phone call at a less busy time.
   —Ask the caller to hold for a brief moment so you can get the clients started on paperwork or escort them to a room.

Returning Calls
♦ Always return calls as promised. When possible, do so within

the next hour but always by the end of the day.

♦ If you cannot answer a query, tell the caller that you will obtain the information and call back with it as soon as possible.

♦ If someone calls with an emergency or urgent situation and you must call them back, ask them to *stay off the phone* so that you can reach them as soon as possible.

Screening Calls

♦ Each practice should establish its own set of guidelines about accepting calls to veterinarians.

♦ Obtain a list of the names of people who must be put through to the veterinarian at once and those whose calls should be returned the same day.

♦ In many situations, your good judgment will be needed, especially in the case of clients who are calling for telephone advice, test results, or follow-up help.

Placing Calls for Others

♦ If placing a call for someone else, write down the details of the information you need to convey or obtain before placing the call.

♦ If you are asked to place a call for someone and then transfer the call to him or her, do so promptly, as this is considered less than ideal business practice. The best procedure under these circumstances is to have the individual for whom you are making the call on the line while you dial or set up a signal—perhaps a series of buzzes—that gets him or her on the line as the second party is answering.

TELEPHONE DOs AND DON'Ts

Do Say. . .
"May I ask who's calling?"
"Who shall I say is calling?"

"The doctor is in surgery right now."
"I don't know, but I can find out if you like."

Don't Say. . .
"Who's this?"
"Who are you?"

"The doctor is busy."
"I have no idea."

FOLLOW-UP CALLS

Follow-up calls can help strengthen your relationship with your clients. You should consider the time you take to make these calls an investment in your job.

When to Call

Individual situations will vary and staff members should be encouraged to use their own judgment on a case-by-case basis. However, the following guidelines are generally appropriate:

♦ *For an animal recovering from a serious illness or injury*—Contact owners within 2 days of the pet's release from the hospital. You can then reassess the situation and determine if and when another follow-up call is needed.
♦ *For an animal recovering from a less serious hospital stay*— Place a follow-up call 4 to 6 days after release.

What to Ask?

Questions should be specifically phrased to elicit key information about the patient's recovery. Speak to the owner clearly and in laymen's terms.

Don't Forget to Listen

Although your clients rely on you for answers to their questions, they also need you to listen. Remember to stop, be silent, and give the client a chance to give you information. Your ability to listen may affect the outcome of a case, because you may glean an important point or two from conversing with an owner.

LONG DISTANCE CALLING

See your telephone directory for area codes and time zones. Call the operator if you need help (either to get the area code of a particular city or to ask in what city a particular phone number is located). Keep different time zones in mind when calling across the country. For most area codes, directory assistance can be obtained by dialing [area code]-555-1212.

Many businesses now have toll-free numbers (beginning with 800 or

888). Using these toll-free lines can save your practice money. Avoid calling numbers beginning with 900, however. These lines charge additional fees.

Region-to-Region Calls

Long distance calling is a service that is provided by a number of companies. These companies are not necessarily the companies that provide local service in a given area. Each long distance company serves designated areas of the country. Contact these companies directly to determine whether they serve your area and for detailed information on their rates and services.

Regardless of the company you choose, the caller may need to dial additional numbers (beyond 1 + area code + telephone number) to access service. This depends on whether Equal Access is provided by your local telephone company as a link with long distance companies serving your area.

International Calls

It is now possible to make international telephone calls to many countries without going through the operator. Direct dialing of international calls is significantly less expensive than operator-assisted calls. To determine whether direct international dialing is available in your area, call the operator.

To place a direct international call, dial as follows:

Access Code	Country Code	City Code	Telephone Number
011	_____	_____	_____

GUIDELINES FOR INTERNATIONAL CALLING

♦ Check the time in the part of the world you are calling.
♦ Write down the access code, country code, city code, and overseas exchange number.
♦ Do not hesitate when dialing; this may result in connection to the wrong number or disconnection.
♦ There may be no tone for several seconds (up to 30) after you dial the last digit.
♦ Instead of one long ringing tone (which you typically hear when making calls within the United States), you may hear two short sounds.

ANSWERING MACHINES

Today, telephone answering devices and voice mail systems are indispensable at many businesses. Services that these systems can provide to veterinary practices include:

♦ **Streamlining the number of incoming calls to the front desk during business hours**—Many systems offer callers several different options (by pressing the number buttons on their phone), such as:

—Accessing emergency help immediately

—Hearing a general information message about the clinic (hours, location, services provided)

—Leaving a message for a member of the staff (the system may have a voice mail feature where messages can be left directly for the appropriate party or messages for all staff are left in one area and must be regularly retrieved and forwarded)

—Being placed on hold until a staff member at the front desk is able to speak with them directly

♦ **Handling off-hour calls**—Instructions regarding emergency calls are absolutely essential when the office is closed. The ability to provide general information and receive incoming messages during these hours is valuable as well.

Bibliography

Shirey JA: The art of listening: A forgotten tool. *Trends,* p 39, Feb/Mar 1992.

FILING AND RECORDKEEPING

The veterinary technician may be responsible for organizing and managing the business aspects of the veterinary practice. The importance of accurate up-to-date recordkeeping and an accessible filing system cannot be overstated. A well-planned system contributes significantly to the efficiency of operation as well as to the hospital image.

The true test of any filing system is whether one can find things when they are needed. Whether records are filed in a computer or in a steel cabinet, they must be readily accessible. Misplaced records can cost a practice inestimable sums in terms of staff time, direct financial losses, and client confidence.

Study your system by taking an inventory of the records in your files. Here are some pertinent questions to consider:

♦ What is the nature of your records?
♦ Where on the premises should they be filed?
♦ Who uses the records?
♦ How often are they used?
♦ How are they used?
♦ How are the records referred to?
♦ What is the size of each record?
♦ How many copies of each record are filed?
♦ Who else has copies of the same record?
♦ How long are the records kept?

Check whether your filing system has any of the following problems:

♦ The information you need is difficult to obtain.
♦ You repeatedly need to expand your file system capacity.
♦ You are maintaining duplicate files of the same information.

- You are using the filing system or equipment for storage of material other than records.
- The file folders/drawers/shelves are too full and do not allow easy access.
- You are not finding the information you require in the first place you look.

Once the analysis is complete, the strengths and weaknesses of your record-keeping system should be clear. The next step is to determine:

- The best way to arrange the records
- The type of material to be filed (paper, computer files, etc.)
- The proper equipment for adequate storage and retrieval
- The proper systems to complement the equipment
- Means and schedule for retaining files

COMPUTER VS. PAPER SYSTEMS*

Records can be stored on paper and/or in computer files. Paper can be damaged by fire or water. It can be misplaced, torn, or crumpled, and it yellows with age. Computer records can be damaged or lost as well. However, they are easy to access, quickly copied, and easily transported. Protect against loss of computer data by:

- Making frequent backups
- Storing backup tapes or disks off-site
- Using write-protection disks
- Creating access passwords to enter the computer system
- Limiting access of personnel to certain parts of the computer system

Ease of Use

Both computerized and paper-based record systems can be easy to use. A business with a small client base may find that a paper filing system is adequate. With a larger client base, files are more easily accessed and managed with a computer system. Computer software allows rapid production of reminder cards, an easy way to sort by any criteria, and

---

*More information about computers can be found in the Equipment section on p. 53.

virtually unlimited expansion in a small space. To maximize the computer's efficiency, input all information directly into the computer rather than writing it down first.

FILING SYSTEMS

Each of the following filing methods has advantages and disadvantages. A systems consultant can help you select the method and the storage and handling equipment that are right for you.

TIPS FOR PAPER SYSTEMS

Materials

♦ **Drawer Space**—A file drawer or shelf should be filled to no more than 90% of its capacity. Tightly packed files slow filing as well as finding.

♦ **Index Guides**—To save time when looking for records, place a guide every 10 to 15 folders.

♦ **Folder Tabs**—Folder tabs should be immediately visible upon opening the file drawer. Folder size/tab style should be uniform throughout. Order supplies for your files that match the ones originally chosen. For clarity, type the tab labels.

♦ **Records per File Folder**—As a general rule, no more than 25 records should be placed in one folder.

Basic Filing Procedure

♦ **Inspecting:** Each document is inspected to see that it is ready to be filed; if not, it should be returned to the appropriate party. Torn papers should be mended before being filed.

♦ **Marking:** The file operator must determine under what name or heading the paper is to be filed and mark the file accordingly.

♦ **Followup and Cross-Reference:** If the record is marked for followup, a note is placed in the followup file. If there is more than one place in which to file the document, make a cross-reference.

♦ **Sorting:** Documents should be arranged in sequence (according to the first filing unit of the name or number) so that they can be placed in the proper folders quickly, without moving back and forth. Sorting also makes documents easy to find if they are needed while out of the file.

♦ **Filing:** Folders should be raised slightly in the file drawer (or removed if on shelves) so that the papers go entirely to the bottom of the folder. Check the caption of both the document and folder as a precaution against misfiling. Place all documents with the tops to the left as you face the folder.

Alphabetic Systems

Alphabetic systems are the most familiar and can be used for any volume of records. Their main advantage is that they provide direct reference to names. One disadvantage is that common names do not occur evenly throughout the alphabet (e.g., more names begin with S than Q). Thus one file may grow cumbersome in size, making identification and location difficult.

Numeric Systems

In numeric systems documents are numbered to distinguish them from one another. Numeric systems can be as simple as numbering from the lowest number and up as needed to the sophisticated system of terminal digit filing (see box below).

TERMINAL DIGIT FILING

Terminal digit filing is a method of arranging numbers in a file so that all numbers ending with the same last digits are grouped together. In this arrangement a six or seven digit number is separated into three groups of numbers by hyphens or spaces:

◆ The last two digits of the number are called the primary number. There are 100 primary numbers, 00 through 99.
◆ The third and fourth digits from the right are called secondary numbers. These also run 00 through 99.
◆ The remaining figures to the left of the secondary number are filed in simple numeric sequence within each group and are called the final numbers.

The following numbers would be filed in the 00 primary and the 20 secondary group:

01-20-00	11-20-00	110-20-00
10-20-00	12-20-00	264-20-00

Advantages of Terminal Digit Filing
◆ All sections of the file expand evenly.
◆ It eliminates periodic back-shifting to take up empty space where records have been removed to make space for new records at the end of the system.
◆ There are fewer misfiles because it is easier to read simple two digit numbers separated into groups.

COLOR CODING

Color coding has become extremely popular during the past few years. It is one of the greatest cost-saving feature developed for the filing and retrieval of records. Color-coding systems can be applied to every method of filing.

Color coding converts numbers or letters to colors. Each digit from 0 to 9 is assigned its own specific color; each letter is assigned two colors. The simple process of filing the folders in a desired sequence creates color blocks. If a folder is filed out of sequence, the color band does not match; thus a misfile is automatically flagged.

Color coding can also be used to index computer disks. This allows you to spot a disk that is misfiled or retrieve one quickly.

Benefits of Color Coding
♦ It eliminates hidden misfiles.
♦ It speeds filing and finding.
♦ Folders are easier to locate while out of the system.
♦ It eliminates the need for index guides.

For paper systems the greatest benefit of a numeric system is speed of filing and finding. It takes twice as long to file and find by name than by number. Although a numeric file requires a cross-index, it can increase efficiency by 40% to 50%.

Numeric systems also provide both a clear, unambiguous identification of the record and a degree of confidentiality.

Subject Filing

Descriptive feature is the focus of this system rather than name or number. A word or phrase is chosen to represent each subject or to point out a distinct aspect of a broader subject. A subject folder may contain any combination of correspondence, bulletins, clippings, pictures, statistics, trade journals, and other printed information relating to the subject.

The subject filing method is considered the most difficult. It demands a complete knowledge of the business and works best if only one person files and retrieves information to increase the probability of finding a given item.

Chronological Filing

Chronological filing is filing by date. This system is usually reserved for copies of freight bills or canceled checks or as a reserve file. It is normally used only where there is little or no reference made to the record once the transaction is complete.

STORAGE OPTIONS
Media Storage for Computer Systems

Look for these features in the equipment you choose for media storage:

- ♦ *Flexibility*—Equipment must continue to meet your needs as the volume of records increases.
- ♦ *Versatility*—Cabinets should be made to accommodate any one type of medium and allow you to mix different sizes in one unit.
- ♦ *Easy Access*—Because labor is the greatest cost in any media storage area, the equipment must provide easy access.

Standard Filing Cabinets

Vertical filing cabinets range from two to four drawers and are available with and without locks and/or insulation for fire protection.

Lateral filing cabinets, now in wide use, offer improved ease and speed of filing when compared with a regular four drawer vertical filing cabinet. Most come in four, five, and six shelf heights.

Open Shelf Filing

Open shelf filing has an obvious advantage in ease of access. It also usually permits filing of odd-sized items such as radiographs and photographs.

Wire Inserts

Wire inserts are available for shelves or drawers. They keep files and documents completely vertical and in many instances displace the expensive suspended pocket (hanging file) system.

RECEIPTS

Most practitioners offer clients three ways to pay for veterinary services: cash, personal check, or credit card. Each has advantages and disadvantages. Cash and checks are used most often and may be preferred by the veterinary hospital because credit card payments cost the hospital a percentage of the transaction as a bank service charge. With credit card payments, however, the hospital does not have to deal with the problem of trying to collect debts.

Cash Payments

Cash payments pose a security risk in that employees may be tempted to pocket the money without recording the transaction. A system should be established so that more than one person monitors the receipts. Obviously, large amounts of cash should not be kept in the veterinary hospital for any length of time.

Payment by Check

When checks are accepted, the following items should be recorded or verified:

- ◆ Client's name
- ◆ Current address
- ◆ Driver's license number
- ◆ Home or work telephone number (or place of employment)
- ◆ Initials of the employee who accepted the check and witnessed the signature.

If you suspect that there might be a problem with the check, contact the client's bank to verify that the checking account has sufficient funds. Most banks will tell you if the check is likely to clear if you give them the client's account number.

Credit Card Payments

When accepting payment by credit card, the following steps should be taken:

- ◆ Verify that the person's signature on the receipt matches the one on the credit card.
- ◆ Check the expiration date on the card.
- ◆ Strictly enforce the rule regarding telephone authorizations on amounts above $50 (or whatever is required by your bank). Approval should be obtained before the client leaves the office.

* * *

On some occasions, it may be necessary to extend credit to clients that cannot pay by any of the above means. The veterinary hospital should have an established policy for extending credit. A complete credit application should be filled out. If the bill is considerable, a deposit of 20% to 25% should be requested from the client.

DIRECTORY OF VENDORS AND SUPPLIERS

Establish a directory of vendors and suppliers. Many comprehensive veterinary practice computer programs have a system for doing so. Other choices include setting up a written system that is stored in some type of file cabinet, or creating a directory using any word processing or database software.

The following categories should be included in the system:

♦ Pharmaceuticals
♦ Biologicals
♦ Diagnostic Supplies
♦ Laboratories
♦ Medical Equipment and Supplies
♦ Nutritional Items
♦ Dental Equipment and Supplies
♦ Office Equipment and Supplies
♦ Maintenance Supplies
♦ Miscellaneous

Under each category, list:

♦ Company
♦ Contact person
♦ Phone number(s) for
    —Ordering
    —Customer Service/Technical Support

For each order made, record the following:

♦ Date of order
♦ Items ordered: size, quantity, price, and any special/bulk discount
♦ Date order received

REASONS FOR MEDICAL RECORDS

Legal Reasons
♦ Many states and some professional associations, like the AAHA, require them.
♦ They are essential in the defense of legal actions for malpractice, negligence, or incompetence.
♦ They are used to establish that a legal contract existed for the care of a patient and collection of a fee.
♦ They are necessary for income and sales tax documentation purposes.

Diagnostic Reasons
♦ They are essential for recording all pertinent facts and diagnostic data so a diagnosis, course of treatment, and prognosis can be established.
♦ They establish information about previous medical problems and management of an ongoing medical ailment.
♦ They serve as a source of data for research.

Business Reasons
♦ They provide information about how to contact an owner.
♦ They provide information for a recall system that will generate income.
♦ They record what services were supposed to be rendered as well as what services were actually rendered.
♦ They can be valued and sold as a depreciable asset of the practice.

MEDICAL RECORDKEEPING

There are many reasons for keeping accurate medical records (see box above). The length of time records should be kept varies with the type of record and with state laws (when in doubt, keep the record):

♦ *Tax records*—Keep at least 7 years.
♦ *Employee records*—Keep for 10 years or as long as the state's statute of limitations.
♦ *Controlled substance logs*—Keep for 2 years.
♦ *OSHA records of injuries or accidents on the job*—Keep 5 years.
♦ *Records of improvements to the property or building*—Keep indefinitely for evaluation of the business if it is sold. (Any records that might be useful to a future purchaser of the practice should be kept indefinitely.)

♦ *Client records*—Keep at least 3 to 7 years after the last transaction. These records are the property of the hospital and the originals must never be given to clients or to another veterinarian. Instead, copies should be made for this purpose.

♦ *Radiographs*—Legally considered part of the permanent medical record and should never be given to a client. However, clients have a legal right to ask for copies. Original radiographs may be mailed to another veterinarian as part of the transfer of records for case referral. Include a preaddressed return mailing label for their return.

Changes to a Record

Changes to a record should be made in a specific way. First, draw a line through the incorrect remarks (do not use white out or try to obliterate the text). Then write your changes in, including the reason for the error.

Components of a Thorough Medical Record

The patient health record may be printed and kept in a filing system, or typed into a computer. A wide variety of preformatted forms and software are available. No matter what medium is used to store the information, it should include several key elements:

Client Information
♦ Name
♦ Address
♦ Telephone numbers (work, home)
♦ Method of payment

Patient Information
♦ General—Name, species, breed, date of birth (preferable to "age"), color
♦ Routine preventive care
   —Vaccinations
   —Treatment for or prevention of internal and external parasites
   —Behavioral consultations
   —Elective surgeries (spay, neuter, declaw)

♦ Physical examination results
♦ Presenting complaint
♦ Problem list
♦ Diagnostic tests and their results
♦ Diagnosis list
♦ Treatment list
♦ Outcome

A sample patient record form begins on p. 42. A thorough medical record will also contain any contracts or consent sheets between the practice and client, telephone consultations that have occurred, anesthesia and surgery logs, radiographs, euthanasia consents, necropsy logs, and any other material pertinent to the case. Finally, any client communications upon release, such as conversations regarding post-surgical care or client handouts regarding at home therapy, should be noted on the medical record.

IDENTIFICATION SYSTEMS FOR HOSPITALIZED ANIMALS

Every veterinary hospital has its own system for tracking hospitalized animals' particular diets and medications. In all clinics some type of card is placed on each animal's cage. The card identifies the animal and gives pertinent patient information. A section is devoted to feeding and medication instructions.

It is of paramount importance that these instructions are clear to all staff. Easy-to-read cards and obvious coding help in alerting personnel to special needs. Color tags, available from cage manufacturers and some petfood companies, are often used to alert staff to the animal's requirements. Each color represents a different need. Consistent recording of what has been administered, including amount and time, should be done immediately after any food or medication is given. Precision in documenting this information must be impeccable to prevent errors.

Identification of individual animals is also important to prevent potentially tragic mistakes. Paper collars are available on which you can write the animal's name.

Special coding may also be used to identify aggressive animals,
(Text continues on p. 46)

PATIENT HEALTH RECORD

Owner _____

Address _____

Home phone _____ Business phone _____

Patient

Species _____ Breed _____ Sex _____ Color _____ Coat _____

Patient name _____ Birth date_____

Year									
DHLPP									
FVRCP									
Rabies									
FeLV									
Heartworm									
Fecal									

Diet and Feeding   **Parasite Control**

_____   _____
_____   _____
_____   _____
_____   _____
_____   _____

Previous Problems (including adverse drug reactions)

_____
_____
_____
_____
_____
_____
_____
_____

MASTER PROBLEM LIST

Prob. No.	Active Date	Problem	Resolved Date Dx	Rx

PHYSICAL EXAMINATION

Presenting Complaint or Request

Date/Time _____ / _____

N = Normal
ABN = Abnormal
NE = Not Examined

1) GEN N ABN NE	2) INTE N ABN NE	3) MUS N ABN NE	4) CIRC N ABN NE	5) RESP N ABN NE	6) DIG N ABN NE
7) GU N ABN NE	8) EYES N ABN NE	9) LYM N ABN NE	10) NS N ABN NE	11) EARS N ABN NE	12) MM N ABN NE

T_____   P_____   R _____   WT_____

Describe abnormalities (Use numbers above.)

_____

_____

_____

_____

_____

_____

_____

_____

_____

_____

Signature _____

TEMPORARY PROBLEM LIST—INITIAL PLAN

Problem	Dx:	Rule outs, Procedures	Rx:	CE

Signature _____

PROGRESS RECORD

OWNER _____

PATIENT _____

CODES

Appetite	Bowel Movement
N = Normal	N = Normal
F = Fair	A = Abnormal
P = Poor	(Specify)
O = None	O = None

Date	App	BM	Temp	Pr#	

those from whom urine or fecal samples are required, and those that require special monitoring.

No matter what system is used, it must be followed assiduously so that no errors occur in feeding or medicating hospital patients.

COMMON ABBREVIATIONS
Common Medical Abbreviations*

activated partial thromboplastin time	APTT
adrenocorticotropic hormone	ACTH
albumin-globulin ratio	A/G ratio
alanine aminotransferase	ALT (Formerly SGPT)
alkaline phosphatase	AP, ALP, alk phos
alpha	α
angiotensin-converting enzyme	ACE
anteroposterior	AP
antinuclear antibody	ANA
aortic second sound	A_2
aspartate aminotransferase	AST (formerly SGOT)
average	avg
barium-impregnated polyethylene sphere	BIPS
basal metabolic rate	BMR
beta	β
blood pressure	BP
blood urea nitrogen	BUN
body surface area	BSA
cardiopulmonary resuscitation	CPR
carbon dioxide pressure (tension)	PCO_2
carbon dioxide pressure (tension), arterial	$PaCO_2$
central nervous system	CNS
cerebrospinal fluid	CSF
cerebrovascular accident	CVA
complete blood cell count	CBC
computed tomography (CAT scan)	CT
creatine phosphokinase	CK (CPK)
deoxyribonucleic acid	DNA

*Use abbreviations such as sid, bid, q4h, etc., only on the patient's medical record. Pharmacists are not familiar with sid. Labels on client medications should be written out (e.g., "twice daily").

disseminated intravascular coagulation	DIC
electrocardiogram	ECG
electroencephalogram	EEG
electromyogram	EMG
ethylenediaminetetraacetate	EDTA
enzyme-linked immunosorbent assay	ELISA
every	q
every day	qd
every other day	qod
every 4 hours, every 8 hours, etc.	q4h, q8h, etc.
eye, each; or both eyes	OU
eye, left	OS
eye, right	OD
focus-to-film distance	FFD
follicle-stimulating hormone	FSH
for example (exempli gratia)	e.g.
French (catheter sizing scale)	F, Fr
fibrin degradation products	FDP
four times daily	qid
gamma-glutamyl transferase	GGT
gastroenterology	GE
gastrointestinal	GI
genitourinary	GU
hematocrit	Hct
hemoglobin	Hb, Hgb
high power	hp
high-power field	hpf
hydrogen ion concentration	pH
identify, identification	ID
idiopathic thrombocytopenic purpura	ITP
immunofluorescent antibody	IFA
immunoglobulin G, A, M	IgG, IgA, IgM
intensive care unit	ICU
international unit	IU
intradermal	ID
intramuscular	IM
intraocular pressure	IOP

intraperitoneal	IP
intravenous	IV
intravenous pyelogram	IVP
lactic dehydrogenase	LDH
left	L
lethal dose	LD
lethal dose for 50% survival of group	LD_{50}
lupus erythematosus	LE
luteinizing hormone	LH
maximum	max
mean arterial pressure	MAP
mean corpuscular hemoglobin	MCH
mean corpuscular volume	MCV
metabolic rate	MR
minimal inhibitory concentration	MIC
magnetic resonance imaging	MRI
mean corpuscular hemoglobin concentration	MCHC
nonprotein nitrogen	NPN
nonsteroidal antiinflammatory drug	NSAID
normal temperature and pressure	NTP
not applicable	NA
not examined	NE
not significant	NS
nucleated red blood cells	NRBC
once daily	sid
over-the-counter	OTC
oxygenated hemoglobin	HbO_2
oxygen pressure (tension)	PO_2
oxygen pressure (tension), arterial	PaO_2
packed cell volume	PCV
per os	PO
plasma protein	PP
premature atrial contraction	PAC
premature ventricular contraction	PVC
pro re na'ta (as needed)	PRN
radioallergosorbent test	RAST
rapid eye movement	REM

recipe (prescription)	Rx
red blood cell	RBC
ribonucleic acid	RNA
right	R
specific gravity	sp gr
standard deviation	SD
subcutaneous	SC
subjective, objective, assessment, plan	SOAP
three times daily	tid
thyroid-releasing hormone	TRH
thyroid-stimulating hormone	TSH
triiodothyronine	T_3
thyroxine	T_4
total protein	TP
twice daily	bid
ultraviolet	UV
United States Pharmacopeia	USP
urinalysis	UA
ventrodorsal (dorsoventral)	VD (DV)
versus	vs.
white blood cell	WBC

Business and Commercial Abbreviations

account of	a/o
account paid	a/p
accounts payable (bills payable)	A/P (B/P)
accounts receivable (bills receivable)	A/R (B/R)
acknowledge	ack
also known as	aka
American Animal Hospital Association	AAHA
American Veterinary Medical Association	AVMA
American Veterinary Medical Association, Student Chapter	SCAVMA
Animal Medicinal Drug Use Clarification Act	AMDUCA
approximately	approx
backordered	B.O.
Centers for Disease Control	CDC

central processing unit	CPU
collect on delivery	COD
doing business as	DBA
Environmental Protection Agency	EPA
Equal Employment Opportunity Commission	EEOC
et alii (and others)	et al.
et cetera (and so forth)	etc.
Food and Drug Administration	FDA
Food Animal Residue Avoidance Databank	FARAD
for your information	FYI
id est (that is)	i.e.
in care of	%
letter of credit	L/C
North American Veterinary Technician Association	NAVTA
Occupational Safety and Health Administration	OSHA
purchase order	P.O.
random access memory	RAM
read-only memory	ROM
World Wide Web	www

Titles

American College of Veterinary Pathologists	ACVP
American Board of Veterinary Practitioners	ABVP
American College of Laboratory Animal Medicine	ACLAM
American College of Veterinary Internal Medicine	ACVIM
American College of Veterinary Surgeons	ACVS
Animal Health Technician	AHT
Bachelor of Arts	BA
Certified Veterinary Technician	CVT
Doctor of Chiropractics	DC
Doctor of Dental Medicine	DMD
Doctor of Dental Surgery	DDS

Doctor of Laws (lawyer)	JD, LLD
Doctor of Medicine	MD
Doctor of Osteopathy	DO
Doctor of Science	ScD
Doctor of Veterinary Medicine	DVM, VMD
Licensed Veterinary Technician	LVT
Master of Dental Surgery	MDS, MSD
Master of Science	MS
Master of Surgery	ChM, MS
Member of the Royal College of Veterinary Surgeons (British)	MRCVS
Registered Pharmacist	RPh
Registered Veterinary Technician	RVT
Veterinary Technician	VT

Units of Measure

ampere	A
angstrom	å (Use nm)
calorie	cal
Celsius (Centigrade)	°C
centimeter	cm
cubic centimeter	cc (use for gas measure)
cubit foot	ft^3, cu ft
cycles per second	c/s
day	d
deciliter	dl, dL
equivalent	Eq
Fahrenheit	°F
fluid ounce (volume)	fl oz
foot	ft
gallon	gal
gram	g, gm
hertz	Hz
horsepower	hp
hour	hr, h
inch	in

international unit	IU
joule	J
kelvin (or kelvin scale)	K
kilocalorie	kcal, Cal
kilogram	kg
kilometer	km
kilowatt	kW
liter	L
meter	m
microgram	µg
microliter	µl, µL
micron, micrometer	µm, µ
milliequivalent	mEq
milliliter	ml, mL
millimeter	mm
minute	min
molar	mol/L
mole	mol
normal (solution)	N
ounce	oz
parts per million	ppm
pint	pt
pound	lb
pounds per square inch	psi
quart	q, qt
roentgen	R
roentgen equivalents man (or mammal)	rem
second	s, sec
square foot	ft^2, sq ft
tablespoon	tbsp, T
teaspoon	tsp, t
torr	Do not abbreviate
unit	U
volume	vol
weight	wt
year	yr

Equipment
and Supplies

OFFICE EQUIPMENT
Computers

Computers consist of two main components: The equipment itself (referred to by the terms *hardware* and *platform)* and the functions or tasks to be processed (referred to by the terms *software, program,* and *application),* which use the hardware to perform the activities and, if desired, store the results.

In a turn-key system the computer and software are purchased as a unit from the same company. Usually the vendor installs the system, verifies that it is functioning properly, and provides staff education. A turn-key system may be easier to get up and running but may be more costly than purchasing components separately.

If software and hardware are selected separately through different vendors, purchasers can buy just the hardware and software they want and they can get better buys. However, this requires a good deal of familiarity with computers and software and does not provide for staff training. Purchasing hardware from a business that provides support in its setup will help.

Hardware

The most important characteristics of the hardware are the *processor speed* (which affects how quickly the computer can perform tasks), *RAM* (amount of memory available while the computer is turned on, which affects the number of activities that can run simultaneously and their complexity), and *internal storage capacity* (the amount of space available for permanent storage of software programs and associated data such as documents, images, or databases). As of the beginning of 1998, a typical high performance computer might include a 300MHz processor, 48MB of RAM, and a 2GB hard drive.

Accessories available as part the internal hardware package include modems for Internet access, different types of disk drives for storage, and CD-rom drives, each with different speeds, capacities, and abilities. CD-roms are important to veterinarians because they can store large volumes of information on a single disk. Types of CD-roms available include compilations of abstracts from the veterinary literature, full journal archives, books, reference libraries, and pharmaceutical information. CD-roms are now in the process of being replaced by the DVD disk, which can store seven to eight times as much data as a CD-rom.

Types of hardware that are connected from outside the computer are called *peripherals*. They include disk drives and modems, as well as items that require larger amounts of desktop space like speakers, printers, and scanners.

Software

Software can perform many activities (composing documents, storing and organizing lists of names and addresses, capturing images, etc.) and is available in packages that perform many kinds of activities or for single, very specialized activities.

The *operating system* is the core instruction set that other software components use to interact with the computer processor. Examples of operating systems include Windows, DOS, Macintosh, OS-2, or Unix-based systems. Different operating environments are compatible with different types of computers and software. It's important that compatibility issues be considered before purchasing a system. For example, Macintosh applications (such as a word processor) will usually not run on a Windows-based computer.

The operating system also determines how the various computer system parts (disks, keyboard, printer, video display, memory, CD-rom, etc.) operate together.

Software packages list the operating systems for which they are written. Some companies provide hybrid software that will run on several different versions of an operating system.

A *database management system* or *practice management system,* the information center in the practice, typically consists of a recall system and inventory control as well as an extended client file and an accounts receivable system. Other types of material that can be stored in the system include national databases of medical information, proceedings of continuing education seminars, and literature abstracts, all available on CD-rom. It's important to check with your vendor to ensure that the memory capability of your hard drive is sufficient.

Computer *diagnostic software* allows input of the results of a physical examination and laboratory tests, then gives a list of differential diagnoses. Other services will allow the veterinarian to electronically send ultrasonic, electrocardiographic, or radiographic images to specialists for their interpretation. These services often require the purchase of specialized equipment.

A *word processing program* let you compose documents. It can be invaluable as both a time-saving and practice-building tool. These kinds of programs can be used to write welcome, thank you, and condolence letters and personalize reminders for checkups and vaccinations.

A *spreadsheet* is an accounting tool. It is used in situations in which data are processed using specified formulas, usually in row/column tabular form.

Computers as Clinic Management Tools

Computer applications in the veterinary practice include the management of medical data and business information. They are used to generate examination, vaccination, and recheck appointment reminders, maintain client lists and inventory control, itemize procedures performed, create invoices, and maintain patient and administrative records. Some clinic management software can also be used with a modem to access the Internet, where a user can get the most up-to-date information in large databases and consult with veterinary specialists and other experts. Types of software programs that might improve hospital efficiency include those designed to address practice management issues or provide diagnostic assistance or those that constitute a formulary of medications and dosages.

Internet Access

The *Internet* is a computer network that allows geographically remote computers to connect and interact. This permits users to exchange electronic mail, browse databases, and search for information. Access to the Internet requires a computer with a modem and telephone line and an account from an Internet Service Provider, such as America Online or Earthlink Network. Veterinary hospitals can set up

THE PAPERLESS PRACTICE

Computers have become an integral part of many veterinary practices across the country. A number of factors have contributed to their increased use. Costs of computer equipment have decreased significantly in the last few years. At the same time storage capacity has multiplied and is now sufficient to hold veterinary hospital records. Finally, software is now flexible enough for both billing purposes and for entering medical records. The ideal of a "paperless practice" may soon become a reality.

Benefits of a Paperless Practice

♦ **Information management:**
—Files for each patient are kept in one place for easy access.
—Use of templates makes patient files more complete. The templates allow you to create a standard space for each data entry point that would be sufficient for practically all patients.
—Misinterpretation of handwritten material is no longer a problem.
—Software is being developed that will integrate findings from the in-clinic laboratory, the outside laboratory, and other sources of diagnostic and medical information into the electronic patient file.

♦ **Client contact/followup:**
—You can quickly bring up a patient's record as needed.
—You can determine whether a pet is up to date on its vaccinations.
—The record will remind you of any existing conditions the pet has.

Considerations

♦ The efficiency of a paperless system is as variable as the people who use it. Anyone who is conscientious about handwriting a note will most likely be equally conscientious about keying it in on a computer. Also, for those who type faster than they write, a computer would obviously better suit their needs.

♦ In most systems any number of people can view a record simultaneously on different monitors. However, for safety purposes, the system should allow only one individual at a time to alter the record.

♦ A chief concern with electronic information is losing it when your hard drive goes down. Adding a second hard drive to your system, which will automatically take over if the first should fail, requires a small investment (as low as $300 to $500).

♦ A computer station is needed in every location where you would enter a medical record or process business information (e.g., examination rooms, the front desk, the laboratory, the doctors' offices).

Information courtesy of Janet Smith and Dr. Al Snyder, IDEXX Laboratories.

THE PAPERLESS PRACTICE *(cont.)*

♦ For practices installing over 7 to 10 workstations the main computer
should be a server-class computer. This type of computer is more expensive than a typical personal computer that you might use at home, but it is
needed to process information from all the workstations connected to the
network.

♦ Computer records are as subject to tampering as hard copies of records. An
extra step of precaution that the staff can take to protect the integrity of the
practice's records is to back up the files at regular intervals (e.g., weekly,
monthly) and store the backup files in a secure area. These backup files
may prove useful should any legal issues arise.

---

their own Internet Web site, which serves a similar function as an informational brochure (see p. 16) but allows updating as desired.

Vendors

Many vendors offer practice management software specifically for
veterinarians. In choosing a computer company, ensure that it is finan-
cially sound and has a good reputation. Ask for references. A company
should also be able to guarantee services and parts for a specified period and offer computer education as needed. Remember to ask about the
cost of technical support.

Photocopiers

The selection of an office copier is complicated by the vast number
of suppliers and different models available. The person responsible for
selecting the right model may not be familiar enough with the technology to make the best decision.

By applying some basic rules, however, the chances of making the
right decision can be increased. Here are a few guidelines about what
to look for when confronted with the task of choosing a copier.

Determine Your Need

Define your needs by calculating the total number of copies you
make during an average month and the type of copying. Most of these
machines copy onto paper that is loaded into the machine in sheet form.
Many different types of paper—plain white bond, colored sheets, or

preprinted materials such as letterhead or forms—can be loaded. The size of the copy that is required can be important, too. If large documents must be copied, you might need a machine that can copy onto larger paper. Normally, however, outsized paper must be placed in files or inserted in documents that are generally smaller in size. The ability of the machine to reduce documents to a more manageable size might be of greater benefit.

Another handy feature is the ability of a machine to make double-sided copies (i.e., copy onto both sides of a single sheet). The bulkiness of lengthy documents can be reduced by up to 50% if this facility is available.

If you collate sets of documents frequently, it might be advisable to select a machine with a collator. A collator can either be an integral part of a photocopier or a separate unit.

Remember that the cost of photocopiers will increase as features are added. When doing cost comparisons, inquire about the cost of on-site service, including any minimum charges, the cost of additional maintenance agreements, and the cost of replacement toner cartridges (including the number of copies per cartridge).

Types of Machines

There are four major types of photocopiers. The first is the tabletop or personal copier. This machine is designed to cater to the needs of one or a few people. It is designed to cope with small volumes (up to 5,000 copies per month) and generally has fewer features.

The second type is designed to cope with medium-volume copying (up to 50,000 copies per month) and is normally mounted on castors. Most of the features discussed earlier can be found on equipment of this size.

The third type, high-volume copiers/duplicators (100,000 copies per month and more), tend to be used in printing shops. These machines not only operate fast but have advanced technologic capabilities.

The last type of copier is used as an output device from a computer. Advanced functions include the creation of logos, letterhead information, signatures, type-style options, and many other functions. The capabilities of these machines are supplied by a very powerful computer.

* * *

Selecting a photocopier does not have to be a major task. If you are satisfied that your supplier is trustworthy and able to provide reliable service, chances are the range of equipment he or she stocks will keep up with technology. Finally, ensure that your contract with the supplier has enough flexibility to allow changes as needed.

Telephones

A wide variety of telephone systems are available. Most veterinary hospitals require a multiline system with advanced features, including an intercom system and voicemail. Telephones should be readily accessible in every room of the hospital.

Intercom systems are extremely useful but are underused because of confusion about their operation. To maximize the usefulness of the intercom system, the following tips are recommended:

♦ Have one person read the operator's manual and conduct training sessions for all employees.
♦ Tack a brief "how to" card near every phone.

Fax Machines

A facsimile (or fax) machine is often used to receive laboratory reports expeditiously or to transmit patient records to another veterinarian. The fax may use the same line as the main telephone or a different one. If the volume of faxes received is low, a fax-phone switcher may be used; this device, which is either part of the fax machine or an external unit, recognizes whether a phone call or fax is incoming and routes it appropriately.

Fax machines use rolls of thermal paper or individual sheets of plain paper. Plain paper machines cost more, but the quality of the material received is much higher and the paper is easier to handle. If you choose a machine that uses thermal paper, make sure it has an automatic paper-cutting feature.

Computers often contain an internal fax-modem. This type of fax limits your transmissions to those that are in computer files. Incoming faxes are received by special software. The ability of the incoming fax information to be transferred to another type of software program varies with the fax software.

MEDICAL EQUIPMENT

The veterinary hospital uses a wide variety of equipment for medical, surgical, and laboratory use. Each piece of equipment must be handled with care, both to extend its life and to ensure its safe and proper use. Clean all equipment after each use (sterilize, if applicable). Routinely test equipment that is seldom used to ensure it is still functioning properly.

Medical equipment available for veterinary practices includes the following:

♦ Otoscope, ophthalmoscope, and stethoscopes
♦ Ultrasound machine
♦ Endoscope
♦ Intravenous fluid delivery equipment
♦ Electrocardiographic machine
♦ Radiographic equipment (machine and developing equipment)
♦ Dentistry equipment

Laboratory equipment may include:

♦ Microscope
♦ Centrifuge
♦ Blood chemistry analyzer
♦ Blood cell counter

Surgical equipment includes:

♦ Anesthetic machines
♦ Surgical instruments

EQUIPMENT MALFUNCTION AND REPAIR

Specific staff members should be given the authority to take care of equipment repair. This prevents loss of work time that may occur if something breaks down and the veterinarian in charge is not available to immediately authorize the repair.

Set up a maintenance schedule for every piece of office and medical equipment. Make sure you know where the instruction manuals are located for all equipment in the hospital. Either store each manual near the specific piece of equipment, or store all the manuals in one place. Along with the instruction manual, include:

♦ Name, address, and phone number of parts supplier and repair person
♦ After hours contact, if available
♦ Technical support phone number, and name of specific person, if possible
♦ Warranty information
♦ Maintenance schedule

PURCHASING AND STORING OFFICE SUPPLIES

Orders are requests for supplies submitted directly to manufacturers or suppliers; **requisitions** are requests submitted to a department or individual within your veterinary hospital.

In maintaining your stock of supplies, try to foresee any special need. For example, you might ordinarily keep 1,000 sheets of letter-head stationery in your supply cabinet. If your clinic is about to initiate a client mailing, however, it would be prudent to place a special order for additional letterhead.

Check your supply cabinet at regular intervals; once a week should be enough for most clinics. Small orders can be expensive to process, but large orders that aren't used for a long time will tie up clinic money. Avoid ordering small quantities of items that are quickly depleted or large quantities of items that are seldom used. Set a goal for frequency of ordering any item, and adjust the quantity ordered based on the amount used over time and any bulk discounts available.

Submitting Requisitions

You probably are required to submit any special order to office management for approval. A special order would be any out-of-the-ordinary request for supplies (e.g., a request for an unusually large quantity of an item or a request for an item that is permanent by nature).

You will also need to requisition supplies if you do not have the authority to order them directly. Time and effort can be saved by using a preprinted requisition sheet. If you do not have such a sheet, you can easily type one up and photocopy it as needed. The sheet should list the supplies you use regularly. All you have to do is check the items needed and enter quantities for each. Special items can be written in.

Placing Direct Orders

If you have the authority to order supplies, you have the responsibility of using good judgment when doing so. Make sure you have ordered the quality and quantity you need at the lowest price. The company with the nicest salespeople may not have the best prices. When comparing vendors, consider both price and service (helpful and knowledgeable salespeople, no-hassle returns, and prompt filling of orders).

In most cases orders are considered standard unless clearly marked "rush." Keep "rush" orders to a minimum; you should anticipate the demand for most of the supplies and place your order for them well in advance.

Receiving Stock

If the delivered goods have been ordered from a manufacturer or supplier, you may have to sign invoices or initial bills of lading. Always check the invoice against copies of the original order to be sure the order is correct. Verify the contents of the delivery by checking them against your form. Sometimes companies accidentally send and bill for items that were never ordered or fail to send those that were. Even the smallest mistake should be brought to the supplier's attention; otherwise, the internal records of your hospital will be inaccurate.

Storing and Distributing Supplies

Effective storage arrangements require orderliness and accessibility. If you permit supply cabinets to become overstuffed or sloppily arranged, you will find yourself losing precious time sifting through a lot of material for the items you need. You will also waste supplies, as some items will be impossible to find and others will be useless because of dust and manhandling.

Here are some tips for storing supplies:

♦ Place dividers on shelves to separate various grades and types of paper.

♦ Install plastic boxes, similar to refrigerator compartments, to hold small items.
♦ Label compartments in each cabinet.
♦ Place new supplies behind older supplies.
♦ Keep frequently used supplies on shelves that are easily accessible. Other items should be kept on the top or bottom shelves or toward the back of shelves.
♦ Maintain inventory control. Both manual and computer inventory systems are available, and many clinics use a combination of the two.
  —Computerized system—Inventory is automatically reduced in the computer's inventory each time a sale is registered.
  —Manual system—Prepare an index or inventory control sheet that indicates what is stored as well as what needs to be reordered. For each item on hand, list the maximum quantity, the allowable minimum, the date last ordered or requisitioned, plus a statement of the time that normally elapses between orders. Keep the index near the supply cabinet and update weekly or monthly.
  —Whatever system is used, a "reorder when X quantity is reached" reminder should be a part of the system.

Many clinics adopt a self-serve policy with regard to availability of supplies. Others have a controlled distribution system, in which only certain people are given access to storerooms and cabinets. These people are responsible for close supervision of the supplies on hand. Their duties include ordering and issuing supplies as needed, recording depletions, and preventing surpluses.

Mail Room Procedures

RECEIVING PACKAGES AND MAIL

Create a policy for handling incoming packages and mail:

- ◆ Record all packages received in a computerized or written file system.
- ◆ Sort mail and packages by importance:
  - —Incoming inventory, drugs, and supplies
  - —Accounts payable (sort by date due)
  - —Accounts receivable
  - —Correspondence
  - —Informational mailings (sort into "keepers" and "junk mail")
- ◆ Compare items received to original orders to be sure order has been correctly fulfilled and to note any items on back order.
- ◆ Promptly refrigerate items that must remain cold.
- ◆ Note damaged goods and request appropriate remedial action.
- ◆ Enter new inventory into computer or on an inventory sheet.
- ◆ Route mail to the proper recipients.
- ◆ Keep track of orders and notify vendors of items not received in a timely manner.

SHIPPING PARCELS

Proper packing and addressing are the best ways to ensure that a package is delivered without delay or damage. A helpful guide, "How to Pack and Wrap Parcels for Mailing," is available free from your local post office.

Two sets of postal scales are usually necessary for accuracy: one for packages up to 2 lb and one for larger packages. Using these in conjunction with current rate charts from your post office or delivery service allows you to prepare packages quickly and easily.

When preparing a package for shipment, be sure to:

♦ **Select the proper container**—The container must be large enough to hold the material being shipped as well as cushioning material; it must also be strong enough to protect the contents during handling.

♦ **Cushion the contents**—Cushioning not only secures the contents (so that they do not move around inside the container), it also absorbs and distributes shock and vibration. When several items are packed in a container, they must be protected from each other as well as from external forces.

♦ **Seal the package properly**—The primary methods for closing boxes and bags include gummed and pressure-sensitive tapes, adhesives, strapping, and staples. Avoid using strings or cords, as they tend to get caught in mail-processing equipment.

♦ **Mark the outside of the package clearly**—The addresses (including the zip codes) of both the sender and receiver should be typed or printed clearly with a marking material that is not readily water soluble or easily smeared. The name and address of both the sender and the receiver should also be included inside the package in case the outside address becomes unreadable or is accidentally lost.

♦ **Include special markings, when appropriate.** Special markings should be indicated below the postage and above the name of the addressee. Examples of these markings include:
—*Fragile*
—*Perishable*
—*Do Not Bend* (protect contents with cardboard backing as well)

DIAGNOSTIC SPECIMENS

Many laboratories have specific requirements regarding specimen shipment, so you should check with your laboratory before sending specimens. Some general guidelines are discussed below.

Clinical specimens and biologic products must be packaged in a securely sealed primary container with appropriate material to withstand shock and pressure changes. The primary container should be surrounded with absorbent material that will soak up leaks. It is then packaged in an outer shipping container with secondary leakproof materials.

Single primary containers must not contain more than 1000 ml (1 quart) of material. No more than 4000 ml (4 quarts) of clinical specimens may be enclosed in a single outer shipping container.

Natural ice will preserve specimens for 18 to 24 hours in cool weather but only for 8 to 12 hours during hot spells. Use dry ice to ship items that need to be frozen. Specimens and ice should be wrapped in separate watertight containers and then packaged together in a larger container for shipment.

Types of specimens that you may need to ship include:

- ♦ **Fresh tissue**—Pack fresh tissue in a box with frozen cold packs. Keep the ice pack close to the tissue but avoid direct contact that might freeze the specimen. The ratio of ice to tissue should be 3:1 (a 2:1 ratio may be sufficient when using a thick Styrofoam container). Paper can be used to further insulate the package.
- ♦ **Serum**—Separate serum from cellular and other contents of blood. Serum should be kept clear and cold.
- ♦ **Whole blood**—For a complete blood count (CBC) or other blood cell work, prepare three thin, air-dried slides and send them with heparinized blood or EDTA blood. Package slides in moisture-proof material.
- ♦ **Specimens for toxicologic analysis**—Most of these specimens should be packed in air-tight glass containers and received at the laboratory frozen. However, tests involving enzyme activity will be inactivated if the specimen is frozen. Contact your laboratory for instructions.
- ♦ **Tissue for microscopic (histopathologic) examination**—Sample tissues should be no more than $\frac{1}{4}$ inch wide. Place samples in 10% formalin. The ratio of formalin to tissue should be 10:1.
- ♦ **Specimens for bacterial culture**—These types of specimens must be shipped in wet ice but not frozen.

POSTAL/COURIER SERVICES

Of the many postal/courier services in the United States the three most well known are the U.S. Postal Service (Post Office), FedEx (formerly Federal Express), and United Parcel Service (UPS). Service offered by some providers may be geographically limited, and fees vary from company to company. Check the yellow pages under "Delivery" and "Air Freight" for listings of service providers in your area.

U.S. Postal Service

The Postal Service offers a variety of mailing services and rates. Pick up a Rate Information Card at your local post office. All packages over 2 lb must be hand delivered to the Post Office or your mail carrier. They cannot be left in mail drop boxes.

Mail Within the United States

Express mail next day service provides delivery by 3 p.m. the next day (except Sunday). Some locations do not have overnight service, so check with the Post Office before sending material. Express mail must be deposited at locations and times designated by the Postmaster and must meet eligibility and preparation requirements.

Priority mail usually reaches any destination within the continental United States within 3 days. The delivery date is not guaranteed. Rates vary by weight and distance. The words "Priority" or "Priority mail" must be placed prominently on the package. For matter sent in a "flat rate" envelope provided by the Post Office, a standard 2 lb rate is

---

CONTACT INFORMATION FOR DELIVERY SERVICES

Post Office
♦ See your local phone book.
♦ Web address of U.S. Postal Service: **www.usps.gov**.

UPS
♦ Service within the United States: **1-800-PICK-UPS (1-800-742-5877)** or **customer.service@ups.com**.
♦ International services originating in the United States and Canada: **1-800-782-7892**.
♦ Web address: **www.ups.com**.

FedEx
♦ For a complete listing of delivery areas, request a copy of the FedEx® Worldwide Directory on diskette by calling **1-800-817-8300**.
♦ Web address: **www.fedex.com**.

charged regardless of distance or weight.

First class mail is generally delivered overnight to cities designated as local and within 2 days to states designated as local. Delivery by the third day is standard for other areas. Rates vary by weight (rounded up to the nearest whole ounce) but not by distance within the United States.

The standard *postcard rate* is lower than the 1 oz first class rate. Postcards must be between 3½ by 5 inches and 4¼ by 6 inches in dimension and from 0.007 to 0.0095 inches in thickness.

Second class mail is reserved for periodicals. The material must be mailed at regular intervals, at least 4 times a year.

Bulk mail rates are available to send large volumes of material (at least 200 pieces or 50 pounds per mailing). Various discounts are offered depending on the number of pieces going to a specific zip code (or related zip code). A detailed booklet describing bulk mailing services is available at local post offices.

Fourth class mail is also known as *parcel post*. Limitations are placed on the type of material that can be sent fourth class: no food class materials, no used checks, and no handwritten material. (If sending an invoice with a box of goods, the invoice should be put in an envelope with a first class stamp, which is then taped to the outside of the box; the box itself carries the fourth class postage for its weight).

Special fourth class mail rates are for shipments of books or videotapes. As with parcel post, no written matter may be enclosed.

Certified Mail

Certified mail provides proof of delivery. The sender receives a receipt at the time of mailing, and a record of delivery is kept at the recipient's post office. A return receipt to provide the sender with proof of delivery can also be purchased for an additional fee. Certified mail service is available only for first class or priority mail delivered within the United States. Only items of no intrinsic value should be sent by certified mail; no insurance coverage is provided against loss or damage. Certified mail with a Receipt for Certified Mail attached can be dropped in any mail box unless an official dated receipt is required.

Registered Mail

Registered mail, the most secure service the Postal Service offers, incorporates a system of receipts to monitor the mail from sender to delivery destination. Registered mail is for irreplaceable items or for those having significant intrinsic value. A receipt is issued indicating proof of mailing, and a receipt for proof of delivery can be requested at an additional fee. Insurance up to $25,000 can be purchased on domestic registered mail. Restricted delivery services are available for additional fees. Registered mail to Canada is subject to a $1,000 indemnity limit. For all other foreign countries, the indemnity limit is currently $42.30. First class or priority mail postage is required on domestic registered mail.

International Mail

All mail to other countries must go via air mail. Call your post office to get rates by country, weight, and type of shipment. Express mail, air mail, postcard, and book rates are available.

Other Services

♦ **Collect on Delivery (COD)**—Used when the mailer wants to collect for merchandise and/or postage upon delivery. COD service can be used for merchandise sent by first class, express, priority, or standard mail. The merchandise must have been ordered by the addressee.

♦ **Merchandise Return Service**—Allows permit holders to pay the postage and fees for merchandise returned to them. The service enables the recipient to return a parcel and have the postage paid by the sender. Under this arrangement the shipper provides a special label with instructions.

♦ **Restricted Delivery**—Indicates that the sender's mail is to be delivered only to a specific addressee or to someone authorized in writing to receive mail for the addressee.

♦ **Return Receipt**—Represents the sender's proof of delivery. A return receipt can be purchased for mail sent COD or express mail or that has been insured for more than $50, registered, or certified. A **Return Receipt for Merchandise** provides a mailing receipt, return receipt, and record of delivery. It is available for merchandise sent at first class, priority, and standard mail postage rates.

U.S. POSTAL SERVICE'S STATE ABBREVIATIONS

State/Possession	Abbreviation	State/Possession	Abbreviation
Alabama	AL	Missouri	MO
Alaska	AK	Montana	MT
American Samoa	AS	Nebraska	NE
Arizona	AZ	Nevada	NV
Arkansas	AR	New Hampshire	NH
California	CA	New Jersey	NJ
Colorado	CO	New Mexico	NM
Connecticut	CT	New York	NY
Delaware	DE	North Carolina	NC
District of Columbia	DC	North Dakota	ND
Federated States of Micronesia	FM	Northern Mariana Islands	MP
		Ohio	OH
Florida	FL	Oklahoma	OK
Georgia	GA	Oregon	OR
Guam	GU	Palau	PW
Hawaii	HI	Pennsylvania	PA
Idaho	ID	Puerto Rico	PR
Illinois	IL	Rhode Island	RI
Indiana	IN	South Carolina	SC
Iowa	IA	South Dakota	SD
Kansas	KS	Tennessee	TN
Kentucky	KY	Texas	TX
Louisiana	LA	Utah	UT
Maine	ME	Vermont	VT
Marshall Islands	MH	Virgin Islands	VI
Maryland	MD	Virginia	VA
Massachusetts	MA	Washington	WA
Michigan	MI	West Virginia	WV
Minnesota	MN	Wisconsin	WI
Mississippi	MS	Wyoming	WY

◆ **Special Delivery**—Available for all classes of mail except express and bulk mail. This service provides for daily delivery including Sundays and holidays as well as delivery beyond normal hours. It is available for all customers served by city carriers and to other customers within a 1-mile radius of the delivery post office.

♦ **Special Handling**—Required for parcels whose contents require additional care in transit and handling, except those sent by first class mail. Special handling service is not necessary for sending ordinary parcels; breakable items will receive adequate protection if they are packed with sufficient cushioning and clearly marked "FRAGILE." Use registered mail with postal insurance for valuable or irreplaceable items.

Addressing Mail

The Postal Service recommends that you capitalize everything, using plain block letters. Omit all punctuation in the address, except for hyphenating nine digit zip codes. Use the common abbreviations recommended by the Postal Service, including standard two-letter state abbreviations (see box on previous page). When a company has a P.O. box number and a street address, make sure that the place where you want the mail delivered appears on the line immediately above the city, state, and zip code line and that it corresponds to the five or nine digit zip code used. Often the zip code for a company's street address and PO box number differ.

Self-Stamping Machine

A self-stamping machine can streamline your mailing process. Although its use saves you money on each individual mailing, that savings must be weighed against the cost of the monthly lease. Look under "Mailing Machines and Equipment" in the yellow pages of your phone book for Pitney Bowes and other postage meter companies.

United Parcel Service (UPS)

UPS offers a variety of services and rates:

♦ **Daily Pickup Service**—Automatic pickup by a UPS driver every business weekday

♦ **On-Call Air Pickup**—A UPS driver is ready to pick up overnight, 2 day, and international shipments on any business weekday.

You can also stop by UPS Customer Counters to ship parcels or use Letter Centers (drop boxes with late pickup times located in key

URGENT DELIVERY OVERVIEW

Overnight delivery service is available from the Postal Service, FedEx, UPS, and several other companies (see yellow pages). Rates vary considerably, so call for pricing and specific services offered. Special services such as weekend, guaranteed next day, or holiday deliveries are often limited to larger cities. Be sure to specify the exact location of both the sender and recipient when making inquiries.

Services available include:

Package Pickup
♦ **FedEx and UPS**—Will pick up overnight packages at your location. Unless you have a regular pickup service, you must call early in the morning or a day ahead to schedule a pickup or take your package to a pickup location.
♦ **Express Mail (Postal Service)**—Items to be sent must be deposited at locations and times designated by the Postmaster.

2 or 3 Day Service
♦ **FedEx**—Guaranteed 2 day service.
♦ **UPS**—Guaranteed 2 or 3 day service where items are tracked.
♦ **Postal Service**—Guaranteed 2 day delivery to areas that cannot be served overnight by Express Mail. The Postal Service attempts to deliver priority mail within 3 days, but it does not guarantee a delivery date and does not track the item unless additional services are purchased (mail is registered or insured).

Weekend Service
♦ **UPS and FedEx**—Provide Saturday delivery only in some areas. Sunday or holiday delivery is possible between selected cities with UPS' "SonicAir" service.
♦ **Postal Service**—Delivers anywhere in the United States on Saturdays. Sunday or holiday delivery is possible with Express Mail (delivery not guaranteed, however).

retail/office areas) for urgent documents and small packages. All UPS shipments are tracked, so you can call and find out the location of a shipment at any time. UPS packages must meet weight and size limitations.

Service Options
The following delivery options are all covered by a money-back guarantee:

♦ **SonicAir Service**—Delivery to any point in the United States and to most international destinations in a matter of hours, 24 hours a day, 7 days a week (including holidays). There are no size or weight restrictions.

♦ **Next Day Air**—Delivery to every address in all 50 states and Puerto Rico. Delivery is guaranteed by 10:30 A.M., noon, or end-of-day the next business day depending on destination (12 or 1:30 P.M. on Saturdays).

♦ **Next Day Air Saver**—Guaranteed next day delivery in the 48 contiguous states, at varying times depending on the location.

♦ **2nd Day Air A.M.**—Used for commercial shipments that must arrive before noon the second business day. It is available in most metropolitan areas of the United States.

♦ **2nd Day Air**—Guaranteed on-time delivery within 2 business days to every address coast to coast and in Puerto Rico.

♦ **3 Day Select**—Guaranteed delivery within 3 business days throughout the 48 contiguous states.

Standard Delivery

UPS Ground Service reaches every address throughout the 48 contiguous states. Delivery time varies from 2 to 10 days depending on location. Deliveries to Alaska or Hawaii require one of the UPS air services.

International Service

UPS offers a variety of services for delivery to international destinations, including urgent and standard delivery. Call for rates by country, weight, and type of shipment. Standard ground service is available between the United States and Canada.

FedEx

FedEx offers a variety of urgent delivery options. All shipments are tracked. Saturday service is available in some areas. Businesses can set up a FedEx account to streamline use of services. Packages can be picked up at the business if a call is made by the appropriate deadline (time varies with location), or they can be placed in a FedEx drop off box by the time listed on the box.

INSURANCE AND HANDLING OF LOST ITEMS

Postal Service

♦ Express mail merchandise is automatically insured up to $500 against loss or damage.

♦ COD mail fees include insurance protection against loss or damage.

♦ Insurance coverage up to $25,000 can be purchased on registered mail. For articles insured for more than $50, a receipt of delivery is signed by the recipient and filed at the delivery post office. A processing fee may be charged if an item is lost and you collect on the insurance.

UPS

♦ UPS automatically tracks all shipments and insures them up to the value recorded on the shipping papers.

♦ Insurance for items up to $100 in value is included in the base shipping price; additional insurance is provided at low cost.

FedEx

♦ FedEx packets are automatically insured up to $100.

♦ Additional insurance may be purchased, but there are limits on certain items and on the type of packaging used to qualify for insurance.

Packaging

FedEx offers a variety of packaging free of charge. The FedEx Letter is 9½ × 12½ and holds up to 8 oz. Larger or heavier documents can be shipped in the FedEx Pak (12 × 15½), boxes (three sizes available), or tube. The FedEx Envelope is a clear plastic packaging for diagnostic specimen shipment. You can also place a FedEx label on your own packaging; check with FedEx on any size/weight restrictions.

Delivery Options

♦ **FedEx First Overnight Service**—Delivery by 8:00 A.M. to 90 major U.S. markets.

♦ **Priority Overnight Service**—Delivery by 10:30 A.M. the next business day to thousands of U.S. cities (noon delivery to most other areas).

♦ **Standard Overnight Service**—Delivery by 3:00 P.M. the next business day to thousands of U.S. cities (4:30 P.M. to most other areas).

- **FedEx 2 Day Service**—Delivery by 4:30 P.M. the second business day (7:30 P.M. to residential destinations) within the continental United States.
- **Dangerous Goods**—Materials that have been identified as "potentially hazardous" by the U.S. Department of Transportation can be handled by FedEx via a wide range of time-definite delivery options.
- **Collect on Delivery (COD)**—FedEx offers COD service with all the above options.
- **Freight Services**—Overnight and 2 day freight service is provided anywhere in the United States. Pieces may weigh up to 1,500 lb each (more with advance approval). International freight service is also available.
- **Live Animal Service**—FedEx's cargo planes are able to handle almost anything, including live animals on a worldwide, airport-to-airport basis.

CLIENT/PROFESSIONAL RELATIONS

Good human relations in veterinary practice depend on the ability of the staff to interact in a positive way with those they encounter on the job. Staff members must not only work well with each other but also deal effectively and amicably with the many types of people who visit the clinic seeking medical services for their pets. Your goal is to create and maintain a high level of goodwill within the practice and to promote a positive image with clients by striving to meet their needs.

EFFECTIVE COMMUNICATION

Effective communication is essential for establishing meaningful relationships with others. Clients and coworkers will not accept your help, advice, or opinions if they cannot relate to you. What you say and how you say it play an important part in establishing rapport and stimulating open communication.

One way to encourage people to share thoughts and feelings and keep the lines of communication open is through the use of "continuing responses." This type of response (1) encourages a person to continue talking and (2) helps to clarify what the person is saying for both himself or herself as well as for the listener.

Three important types of responses fall into the category of continuing responses:

♦ A **simple encourager** is the easiest response. It communicates "Go on; I'm listening and I understand." Nonverbal encouragers include smiling or nodding in understanding or agreement. (On the other hand, frowning, looking puzzled, or folding your arms and positioning your body away from the speaker will have the opposite effect.)

♦ A **content response** attempts to help you and the person to whom you are speaking understand what has just been said. In this response, you mirror or echo the content of what you just heard.

For example, suppose a client says "I'm not sure what to do. If I don't leave Bootsy overnight in the hospital, I'll have to travel back here in the morning so he can have those tests. But he'd be happier staying at home with me tonight."

By asking a question such as "Did I understand correctly? You are concerned that ..." and then stating what you perceive as the problem, you will elicit information that you otherwise might not obtain. Is the client worried about Bootsy's being scared? Is she frightened of being alone? Is she angry about having to make another trip? If you simply say, "Look, it will be OK. We'll take good care of Bootsy," you will never find out.

♦ An **affective response** is the most difficult to master because you must be aware not only of the content of the client's communication but also the "affect" (feelings) within that communication. Therefore you must listen to what the client says and how he or she says it.

It is important to focus on feelings, which are sometimes hard to discern. Listen not only to what is said but the tone of voice. Also, try to imagine how you might feel in the same situation. When you think you have identified a possible feeling or emotion, put it into words. Use sentences that begin with "It sounds like ..." or "Perhaps you are saying ...." If you are wrong, the client will be able to tell you so and then has an opportunity to clarify how he or she feels.

Role-playing can be helpful in learning to communicate effectively. Ask a coworker to play the role of a client and act out a typical hospital situation. Then practice responding, first, with a simple, encouraging statement and then by giving either a content or affective response. Do this until you feel comfortable with your responses and until your responses come naturally.

MEDICAL INSTRUCTIONS AND COMPLIANCE

Although it is usually the veterinarian's role to inform clients about a pet's condition, technicians are frequently called on to discuss a pet's illness with clients or to interpret facts and information for them. Therefore it is essential for technicians to know how to provide clients with this information as well.

A crucial aspect of offering information to clients is to verify that understanding has taken place. This can be achieved by having the client repeat the information or demonstrate the instructions for you.

It may be necessary to repeat information several times. Many clients are unable to absorb information the first time it is given because it triggers upsetting feelings that block reception. The most intelligent individuals can become incapable of absorbing information when their beloved pet's life is threatened.

It is important to know that people are more likely to remember what they hear than what they have read, and what they say is generally retained even longer than what is heard or read. Therefore having clients repeat the medical information helps them remember it and lets you know if they have understood you.

In many cases the information may be too overwhelming for clients to digest in a brief period. Owners should be given detailed written instructions about their pet's care to take home with them. They can refer to this resource as needed. Clients should also be encouraged to call the clinic if any questions or problems arise.

PROBLEM ENCOUNTERS

Many technicians and veterinarians agree that the greatest source of stress in veterinary practice arises from problematic interactions between them and pet owners.

By virtue of your importance to clients and the nature of your work, you, the technician, are a counselor. While not professional counselors by training, technicians and assistants are on the front line for upset, confused, grieving, emotionally ill, or immature clients.

In all such situations it is important to keep some fundamental principles in mind.

- ♦ It is essential to accept a person, maintaining an attitude of warmth and goodwill, whether or not his or her way of behaving is socially acceptable or to your personal liking.
- ♦ Clients have a right to self-determination. This means that, while

you can advise them about an animal's care or well-being, the final decision should be their own personal choice.

The Irate Client

Maintaining a position of unconditional positive regard for some clients can be a difficult task. It takes practice to refrain from returning anger or to avoid being defensive when a client is expressing hostility.

In your professional role you must not take a client's anger personally. Instead, consider what the client is feeling, that is, what is going on beneath the anger. Pausing to look at the situation in this way will free you to resolve tense situations more easily.

The basic principles of effective understanding are:

♦ Observing (what the person does)
♦ Listening (to what and how something is said)
♦ Empathizing (how does the person feel?)
♦ Interpreting (what is the person really trying to say?)

Anger is primarily an expression of an unmet need or frustrated goal. When an expression of anger is misunderstood, the resulting disruptive energy can spread like flu and affect everyone in its path.

Some people have a greater capacity than others for coping with disruptive energy. Nevertheless, everyone has a saturation point beyond which they can no longer handle the situation. At this point the person becomes angry or hostile.

When owners attempt to deal with a pet's illness or injury, they can experience an enormous amount of stress. Thinking that a beloved pet could be chronically sick, disabled, disfigured, or die is a highly threatening and anxious experience. Since owners must now depend on the hospital to deal with the pet's problem, they may also feel powerless, which is another component of anxiety.

More anxiety arises if the pet must be hospitalized. Most owners are unhappy about the separation from their pets, and some owners may even feel fear if the pet serves as a protector.

Hospitals require routines, uniformity, and standardization to run efficiently, but these same aspects can make health care seem impersonal, complex, and frustrating. All of these factors can contribute to a client's anger.

The intensity of anger depends on the degree of the threat. Because society frowns on overt displays of anger, it may be expressed in demanding, uncooperative behavior rather than in the form of rudeness, sarcasm, or verbal attack. Angry clients may direct their energy at members of the health care team and the target of the anger might not be the cause. It is not unusual for a receptionist or technician to bear the brunt of anger actually aimed at the veterinarian who may not be on hand at the moment or who cannot come to the phone when an anxious client calls.

Extreme tact on the part of the veterinary professional is required to verbalize frustrated or angry feelings without attacking the client. "I" statements, expressing your own thoughts and feelings, such as "I really feel frustrated..." are less threatening than "you" statements that attack and prompt defensiveness, such as "You make me feel frustrated."

If staff members can honestly and openly share personal feelings and reactions (e.g., "I really feel frustrated that everything we do seems wrong; can you help us help you better?"), clients may be more willing to explore and disclose the cause of their behavior.

After you have said what is required, give the other person plenty of time to respond and share his or her perspective. If the response makes you feel attacked, resist the desire to fight back! If your client starts screaming, you can defuse the situation with sincere words to this effect:

> "I want to listen to you, but it is hard to do when you are yelling at me so loudly."

This approach usually works beautifully; if it does not, tell the person again that you want to listen and that you will be glad to return when he or she has calmed down ... then walk away.

Money Disputes

The veterinary staff's best defense against clients becoming disgruntled over the bill is information. Before any procedure is undertaken, the fee for that measure should be discussed with the client. Do not forget to remind the client that such fees are over and above any base fee for the veterinary visit. Also advisable is presenting the client with a written itemized estimate. Some practices have instituted a policy of posting fees for veterinary services in the reception/billing area to further counteract the possibility of an unpleasant surprise on the part of the client.

Of course, these measures will not avert all disputes because of the very nature of the stressful health care environment and the differing personalities the staff must deal with. When difficulties arise, remember the guidelines for dealing with anger. In addition, do not criticize clients or dismiss their problems and feelings.

Don't say...	*Do say...*
"We gave you an estimate of the final bill ... Why are you reacting so strongly to the cost?" (critical)	"I know that sometimes it's hard to realize how costly veterinary medicine can be." (nonjudgmental)
"The estimate we gave you was just that, but it was very close. Why are you so upset over $15? (critical)	"I'm sorry that our estimate was a bit off. It's sometimes difficult to anticipate every need the pet might have. Can we help you with a payment plan perhaps?" (supportive)

NOTE: Make sure you discuss any options like payment plans with the veterinarian beforehand.

Client Grief*

Many emotional and physical reactions to a pet's death are typical and normal, including feelings of great fatigue and drastic changes in sleeping and eating patterns. Normal grief reactions also can include mental confusion and hallucinations.

When a companion animal dies, the grief can be as intense as the grief felt when a family member or friend dies. The pet owner may experience some or all of the five stages of grief identified by Elizabeth Kübler-Ross (see box on p. 82).

*Portions of this section are based on excerpts from "When a pet dies: Understanding and helping your client's grieving process." Waltham Int Focus, vol 2, no 3, 1992, and the "Human Relations" series of articles by Dr. Carole Fudin that appeared in Veterinary Technician. Dr. Fudin is a psychotherapist specializing in the psychologic aspects of veterinary practice and in the human-animal bond.

STAGES OF GRIEF

Stage 1—Numbness and Denial

When a terminal illness is diagnosed or death occurs, the pet owner may not accept the reality of the situation. This first stage is characterized by feelings of shock, denial, and disbelief. Owners experiencing numbness and denial may look and feel dazed. When the prognosis is poor, some owners may express a desire to get a second medical opinion.

Clients in this state do not need to be corrected or convinced to face the truth. Veterinary hospital staff should provide direct statements such as, "I know it's hard to believe that Buttons is dead."

Stage 2—Anger

Anger may be focused at the hospital staff—pet owners may blame the staff for not being able to cure their pet or for not discovering the illness sooner. The source of the client's anger is legitimate and needs to be understood and dealt with compassionately.

Veterinary hospital staff must not avoid the client or react defensively; the client's grief will be complicated and the relationship between staff and owner will be strained. If turned inward, anger causes guilt. Owners should be made aware that their guilt reflects their desire to undo the situation.

Stage 3—Bargaining

The client may make promises to do good works if the pet is saved or even make bargains with God. Clients may consent to expensive procedures and treatments even though the chances for recovery are slim.

Stage 4—Depression and Grief

This stage is characterized by a client's intense sadness as the death of the pet approaches or occurs. The client's reaction will be influenced by the closeness and duration of the relationship and by the support available to him or her.

In some cases, the veterinary staff may be a client's only source of comfort. It is important to ask if the client has people who know and understand the relationship with the pet. A hospital staff member may need to assume the role of comforter for the client.

Stage 5—Acceptance or Resolution

After an appropriate amount of time has passed, the client may reach a new level of grief. In this stage, the client no longer feels anger, guilt, or intense pain about the pet's death and is able to reminisce and look at objects that belonged to the pet.

One sign of acceptance is the owner's ability to objectively evaluate the appropriateness of getting a new pet.

What to Do for a Grieving Client

Intense grief begins within a few hours. Within 14 days, the grief usually peaks in severity. Many veterinary hospitals send cards to grieving owners or telephone these clients. One recommendation is to telephone the client within the first 3 days of the pet's death and then again after 3 weeks. A more passive approach is to await contact from the owner.

It is helpful for grieving owners to know that it is normal to feel physically ill and emotionally depressed for a while. The hospital staff should reassure the grieving client that feelings of helplessness or hopelessness, irregular sleeping and eating habits, mental confusion, and hallucinations are normal.

If grief is so intense that it seriously disrupts the client's life, however, professional help may be necessary. Severe depression for more than 3 weeks or suicidal thoughts or feelings should prompt recommendations to seek such help. Be aware that people with other major stresses (divorce, illness of a family member, etc.) are more likely to need additional help. Make a simple statement such as "If you need help handling your sorrow, let us know and we can direct you to some resources." Be ready to offer the name of:

♦ A local grief counselor
♦ Pet loss support hotlines (see the AVMA Directory)

PROFESSIONAL LIABILITY (MALPRACTICE)

Liability is defined as one's obligation or responsibility according to the law. Malpractice is defined as "professional misconduct or unreasonable lack of skill," which in practical terms means failure to exercise the degree of skill, learning, and care applied by the average prudent, reputable member of the profession. It is important for the veterinary technician to be aware of his or her personal liability as well as steps that can be taken to minimize the chances of a malpractice suit.

The Professional Liability Policy

The owner of the veterinary hospital should have a professional liability insurance policy, which covers such malpractice risks as acts of

REDUCING THE RISK OF MALPRACTICE LITIGATION

The following guidelines were developed by the AVMA Professional Liability Insurance Trust with the goal of preventing malpractice situations from arising and, in the event of litigation, improving the chances for a successful defense.

Before Treatment

♦ No statement should be made that can be interpreted as a guarantee of results.

♦ The client should be advised of the risks before proceeding.

♦ The owner's written consent should be obtained before surgery is performed, anesthesia is induced, marked changes in treatment are made, or the animal is euthanized.

♦ Veterinarians should not represent themselves as specialists unless they are willing to be held to a higher standard of skill and competency than other veterinarians.

♦ Inquiries should be made as to whether the animal has been under the care of another veterinarian; if so, such records should be obtained.

♦ Treatment should not begin without the proper equipment. If necessary to proceed, the client must be advised of the facts and risks involved; it is important to document in writing that such disclosure has been made.

♦ Appropriate identification techniques must be used to avoid treating the wrong animal.

During Treatment

♦ Detailed and accurate records of treatment of animals in the practice's care, custody, or control must be kept, including the exact dates (by month, day, and year) of treatment.

♦ Avoid having the client assist you—particularly when restraining animals.

After Treatment

♦ Avoid mentioning other treatments if the original treatment was unsuccessful.

♦ With the permission of the owner a necropsy should be performed when the cause of death is in question; use of a veterinary pathologist is recommended.

♦ Avoid apologetic statements or excuses. Do not admit fault.

♦ Indicate concern for the owner.

♦ Pressing a client for payment of a bill for professional service often invites a malpractice claim. PROCEED CAUTIOUSLY. Records should be reviewed and evaluated in the light of a possible malpractice claim.

REDUCING THE RISK OF
MALPRACTICE LITIGATION *(cont.)*

♦ Do not release original records or radiographs to the owners or their representatives.
♦ Call the Professional Liability Insurance Trust Office immediately upon the occurrence of any event that could give rise to a claim. Any expression of dissatisfaction by a client is sufficient reason for notification.

Potential Claim
♦ No statements should be made about settlement of a malpractice charge simply to avoid ill will. Such statements could prejudice the case.
♦ Report the claim promptly to your liability insurance carrier.
♦ Cooperate fully with the claim representative.
♦ Do not discuss any possible malpractice case, even those that do not involve you, with clients or attorneys.

General
♦ Label all dispensed products. Include warning: "Keep out of reach of children," and if product is highly toxic to humans, mark it "Poison." Use child-resistant packaging whenever possible.
♦ Keep up with standards in the field of veterinary care—what was good practice 10 years ago may be completely outmoded today.
♦ Be familiar with federal, state, and local laws that could affect the practice, including waste disposal, service of radiologic equipment, drug labeling and storage, and dispensing of controlled substances.

---

omission (e.g., failure to perform adequate diagnostic tests), acts of commission (e.g., amputating the wrong limb), and improper or inadequate restraint of an animal resulting in injury to the owner. When acting in their capacity as employees of the practice, technicians are covered by the hospital's professional liability policy even when they are sued individually or separately from the hospital (which is highly unlikely because the chances of recovering damages are poor).

Standard exclusions from a professional liability insurance policy include illegal acts, operating under the influence of drugs or alcohol, and guaranteeing results. Most policies also exclude theft, escape, and injury or death of hospitalized animals from causes other than those related to treatment; additional coverage can be obtained for these situations.

It is recommended that professional liability insurance be purchased from association carriers, such as the American Veterinary Medical Association's (AVMA) Professional Liability Insurance Trust. For covered claims, the AVMA's malpractice insurance policy provides defense, covers the full cost of such defense, and pays amounts required to settle claims and satisfy court judgments (up to the policy limits). For more information on this program, contact a service representative toll-free at 1-800-228-7548. Other veterinary associations also offer professional liability insurance programs.

SEXUAL HARASSMENT

Sexual harassment is a form of sex discrimination prohibited by federal, state, and local law. The Equal Employment Opportunity Commission has issued guidelines under Title VII of the Civil Rights Act of 1964 concerning sexual harassment. The guidelines state that unwelcome sexual advances, requests for sexual favors, and other verbal or physical conduct of a sexual nature constitute sexual harassment when:

♦ Submission to such conduct is made either explicitly or implicitly a term or condition of an individual's employment.
♦ Submission to or rejection of such conduct by an individual is used as the basis for employment decisions affecting the individual.
♦ Such conduct has the purpose or effect of interfering with an individual's work performance or creating an intimidating, hostile, or offensive work environment.

Sexual harassment includes, but is not limited to:

♦ Verbal harassment (epithets, derogatory statements, jokes, threats, slurs), including verbal requests, demands, discussions, or comments, whether face-to-face or over the telephone
♦ Physical harassment (touching, pinching, assault, physical inter-

---

THE FACTS ABOUT SEXUAL HARASSMENT

♦ Most harassers are men, but most men are not harassers.
♦ Intentional harassment is an exercise of power, not romantic attraction.
♦ Of all harassment incidents, 90% involve men harassing women, 9% involve same-sex harassment, and 1% involve women harassing men.

ference with normal work or movement)

♦ Visual harassment (posters, cartoons, calendars, drawings)
♦ Sexual innuendo and demands for sexual favors (unwelcome sexual statements or advances)

Sexual harassment is prohibited whether directed toward men or women and whether the employee accepts or rejects the advance.

Preventing Harassment in the Workplace

The first step in preventing sexual harassment is open discussion and acknowledgment of the potential for a problem. Your hospital should have a written policy to ensure that harassment issues are clearly and definitively addressed. The policy should include:

♦ A definition of sexual harassment
♦ A reporting procedure for victims of harassment
♦ Procedures to follow after sexual harassment is reported
♦ Alternative courses of action for special circumstances such as the following:
　—When the person to whom the harassment should be reported is the harasser
　—When the problem persists or inadequate action is taken

Organizations that have a written policy and grievance procedures and that offer sensitivity training are less likely to be held liable in sexual harassment civil cases.

SUBSTANCE ABUSE

Precautions should be taken to prevent the illegal use of drugs that can be obtained in the workplace. Numbered prescription blanks ensure that prescriptions are carefully monitored, and routine cross-checking of controlled substances logs ensures that the amounts used are adequately accounted for.

If you notice signs of potential substance abuse, notify your supervisor. Problems noted in a veterinarian should be brought to the attention of a confidential reporting agency in your state. For more information, call your state veterinary association or contact the AVMA at

---

SIGNS OF SUBSTANCE ABUSE AT WORK

- ◆ Personality changes
- ◆ Increased tardiness
- ◆ Frequent number of sick days
- ◆ Job-related mistakes and accidents
- ◆ Decreased productivity
- ◆ Complaints from clients and other staff members
- ◆ Physical and psychological reactions to substance (e.g., trembling, sweating, weight loss, euphoria, paranoia, depression, confusion, chronic fatigue, lack of interest in work/outside activities)
- ◆ Discrepancies in controlled substance records

1-800-248-2862 (ask about the impaired professionals program).

Bibliography

Bravo E: *The 9 to 5 Guide to Combating Sexual Harassment*. New York, John Wiley & Sons, 1992.

Hannah HW: Legalese in malpractice cases (legal brief). *JAVMA* 190(7): 850–852, 1987.

Kübler-Ross E: *On Death and Dying*. New York, Macmillan Publishing Co., 1969.

Lynch F: *Draw the Line: A Sexual-Harassment-Free Workplace*. Grants Pass, OR, Oasis Press, 1995.

Model Policy on Harassment, in *AVMA Membership Directory and Resource Manual*. Schaumburg, IL, 1997.

Wagner E: *Sexual Harassment in the Workplace: How to Prevent, Investigate, and Resolve Problems in Your Organization*. New York, AMACOM, 1992.

Wilson JF, O'Brien JP: Crisis protection, in Wilson JF (ed): *The Solvay Business Guide for Veterinary Practice*. Lawrenceville, NJ, Veterinary Learning Systems, 1983, pp 127–136.

PERSONAL MANAGEMENT

TIME MANAGEMENT

Making the best use of every part of your working day requires planning and discipline. For many individuals, a well-kept calendar is the key to organization. The calendar may be the ideal place to store notes, addresses, and telephone numbers that otherwise might be jotted down on loose sheets of paper and possibly lost. You may also find it helpful to record your "to do" list in the calendar, or you may prefer to keep this list in a separate notebook.

Time Management Tips
General

♦ At the end of each day make a list of what you intend to do the next day. Prioritize the list, decide which of these are a "must" for the next day, and make sure you complete them as planned.

♦ Delegate your work when appropriate. Describe delegated work completely and clearly to minimize confusion and mistakes. Assign the right people to the right jobs. Make sure that subordinates know how to do the job right.

♦ Don't assume an impossible workload. Let your supervisor/ other staff members know when you need help or can't take on extra work.

♦ When planning your schedule, provide time for unexpected developments.

♦ Do not procrastinate. For example, make a habit of answering correspondence/phone calls the same day.

♦ Do one task at a time.

♦ Strive for excellence, not perfection. It is better to get more things done well than one thing done perfectly.

♦ Try to block out periods of time for related activities. For example, make phone calls at the same time when possible.

♦ When interrupted, make a note of where you are on a task so you will know where to start again later.

♦ Minimize interruptions by letting others know the best time to contact you.

Telephone Efficiency

♦ Place your outgoing calls in priority order.

♦ Keep a list of frequently called numbers by the phone.

♦ Keep a pad and pencil next to your phone at all times.

♦ Use a bound phone memo book instead of separate memos.

Managing the Workplace

♦ Organize your desk so that you don't spend time looking for things.

♦ Clear top of desk of all work except the specific task you are working on.

♦ Throw away unnecessary paper, files, etc. When in doubt, throw it out!

♦ Don't handle a piece of paper more than once. Decide what to do and put it away.

♦ Skim through reading material and read only those pieces related to your job.

COPING WITH STRESS

The veterinary technician is very likely to suffer from tension and anxiety at times, as the profession is frequently a highly stressful one. Tension becomes a problem only when it is chronic and times of joy and relaxation are few. In such cases "burnout" is not far off.

The human body can respond to too much pressure in innumerable ways. Headaches, indigestion, palpitations, diarrhea, and eczema are common and early signs of excessive stress. Some sufferers complain of symptoms such as depression and anxiety. After extended periods stress can lead to the development of serious disorders such as severe asthma, chest pains, and ulcers. These manifestations of stress will never be completely resolved until the underlying problem is addressed.

Burnout victims are accomplishers and doers. They have no room

DEALING WITH WORK STRESS

Common sources of work stress and suggestions for dealing with them are listed below:

You no longer enjoy your work	Try to determine what upsets you most and what you would prefer to do.
You're having a problem dealing with people around you	Discuss the situation with a friend, the personnel manager, your boss, or the individual with whom you are having difficulty.
	Consider whether your attitude might be causing the problem.
You're not sure what you want out of your career or job	You may think that you've chosen the wrong career, but the real problem may be that you are unhappy with certain aspects of your job.
	Talk with your veterinarian or others in your practice about varying and expanding your job responsibilities.
	Discuss the problem with others in your field.

for anything they consider as weakness. On the surface a burned-out person may not be a very pleasant or sympathetic personality. He or she is often cranky, critical, angry, rigid, and resistant to suggestions and advice.

Burnout is nothing to be ashamed of. People who fall victim are individuals who have tried hard to reach a goal. They are usually the ones who can always be counted on to do more than their share. They often have pushed themselves too hard and for too long.

Juggling Work and Home Life

This area can be a real challenge and a source of great anxiety. If it is a problem for you, set priorities and become more organized and efficient at work and at home. If you are married and find yourself shouldering most of the burden of chores and child care, devise a system in which you and your spouse can share these duties more equally.

FAMILY AND MEDICAL LEAVE ACT

The Family and Medical Leave Act of 1993 requires businesses to provide unpaid leave to eligible employees for family or medical reasons (e.g., care of a newborn or elderly family member). For information about how this might apply to your situation, call 1-800-959-FMLA.

Don't allow your job to become all encompassing or a substitute for self-confidence. Never forget that you are much more than your work.

A Nine-Point Plan for Dealing with Stress

Everyone experiences signs of prolonged stress at one time or another. If you notice a persistent pattern in your stress reactions or if the intensity of your reactions seems excessive, don't ignore it. Use your awareness as a first step toward managing stress.

To start, consider the following plan:

♦ Recognize when problems are developing and what the early warning signs of stress are for you. Do you get a headache, can't sleep, feel irritable?

♦ Limit your exposure to stress. Cut back your commitments, reduce your workload, or resign from a committee or two.

♦ Remember that your life has four cornerstones—family, work, leisure, and friends. When planning changes to the structure of one, be careful not to jeopardize another.

♦ Plan your life more efficiently. Make lists. Think of the things that annoy you most and try to work out how you can solve the problems before they develop.

♦ Relax your body. When you are under pressure, your body becomes tense. By learning to relax your muscles in private when you are not stressed, you will enable yourself to relax them in public when you're under pressure.

♦ Relax your mind. Sit with your eyes closed and daydream.

♦ Keep as physically fit as possible.

♦ Take a break at least once a week, and take a weekend off every now and then. When you have a vacation, make sure it is a true vacation.

♦ Don't always hide your feelings. Frustration is a major cause of stress, so let your voice be heard.

Remember that you need some degree of stress in your life. Problems arise only when the amount becomes excessive, a level that varies from person to person. Become attuned to your own threshold for coping and you will enjoy life more fully.

Continuing Education

Continuing education can help keep your job fresh and help you avoid burnout. Choose an area you find interesting and that your supervisor thinks will help improve the practice. Pursue that area by attending meetings, reading, or watching educational videos.

The AVMA has a wide variety of educational videos that are available on loan. See the *AVMA Membership Directory and Resource Manual* for the list and directions for ordering.

PROJECTING A PROFESSIONAL IMAGE

Technicians should project and maintain a professional image, which includes their health and appearance. A polished professional image contributes positively to the practice.

Posture and Presence

Because hospital staff members spend most of their time interacting with clients, their posture and presence must be fine-tuned. You may be the first person a client sees and therefore the first one to make an impression. Remember that clients react to you based on how you look. A professional-looking staff member will be treated professionally.

Attire

Some hospitals provide specific guidelines for appropriate clinical attire, whereas others provide staff members with a specific work wardrobe. In both cases there is a standard appearance the hospital director wants employees to uphold.

Even if such guidelines are absent, staff members should strive to maintain a level of professionalism in their dress. What you wear should fit your duties but still project a professional image. Obviously, corporate attire is not appropriate here but neither are cut-off jeans. You should exercise your judgment and consult your hospital director for specifics.

In general, clothing that would in any way hinder you in your regular duties is not appropriate. Your attire should be comfortable and loose fitting yet always clean and not wrinkled. Periodically, check your clothing for stains. Wear shoes that are comfortable and make sure they are clean. Excessive jewelry or makeup should be avoided as should heavy application of fragrance products.

Personal Hygiene

The importance of personal hygiene in the veterinary hospital should not be underestimated. Upon entering each examination room, technicians should thoroughly wash their hands with an antibacterial soap. Hands should be washed both before and after handling each patient to discourage the spread of organisms.

The veterinary technician can play a key role in all preparatory aspects of surgery and surgical assistance. The purpose of the scrubbing procedure, an essential prerequisite to surgery, is to remove dirt and organisms from the hands and arms.

Nails and cuticles must be kept short. Before beginning the scrub, jewelry must be removed. Any visible soil should be removed during the scrub. If, after the scrub has begun, the hands touch an unsterile object, the process must be repeated.

Bibliography

Fair EW: Efficiency requires planning, teamwork, and evaluation. *Vet Tech* 11(3):159, 1990.

Kagan KG: Aseptic technique. *Vet Tech* 13(3):207, 1992.

CREATING A SAFETY PROGRAM

A written policy about worker safety and accident prevention will benefit the entire hospital. The Occupational Safety and Health Administration (OSHA) is the federal agency responsible for publicizing known hazards of each profession. By law employers are required to provide a safe and healthful workplace and follow OSHA-mandated standards (as compiled in the OSHA Work Practice Guidelines). Specific guidelines, such as those for handling cytotoxic agents (e.g., chemotherapeutic agents) are published in Technical Assistance Bulletins that can be obtained from OSHA (see box below).

Your state may also have specific laws regarding first aid, safety, or

---

HOW TO CONTACT OSHA

♦ To report suspected fire hazards, imminent danger safety and health hazards in the workplace, or other job safety and health emergencies, such as toxic waste in the workplace, call OSHA's 24 hour hotline: **1-800-321-OSHA**

♦ Information about and copies of the Occupational Safety and Health Act of 1970, specific OSHA safety and health standards, and other applicable regulations may be obtained from the nearest OSHA Regional Office:

Atlanta, GA	(404) 347-3573	Kansas City, MO	(816) 426-5861
Boston, MA	(617) 565-9860	New York, NY	(212) 337-2378
Chicago, IL	(312) 353-2220	Philadelphia, PA	(215) 596-1201
Dallas, TX	(214) 767-4731	San Francisco, CA	(415) 975-4310
Denver, CO	(303) 844-1600	Seattle, WA	(206) 553-5930

♦ OSHA Technical Assistance Bulletins can be obtained by writing to **Director of Technical Support, Room H-3651, Washington, DC 20210** or to your state OSHA office (check the blue pages in your telephone book).

♦ Web site: **www.osha.gov**

---

accident prevention in the workplace. Regulations may include requirements for:

♦ One or more staff members to be certified in basic first aid
♦ Number, contents of, and location of first aid kits
♦ Accident prevention or hazard communication programs

Safety training materials may be available. Contact the Department of Labor in your state for details.

A hazard communication program ensures that employees are advised of potential workplace hazards. The program may enlist the use of the "AVMA Guide to Hazard Communication,"* a list of hazardous chemicals, and Material Safety Data Sheets (MSDS), labels, and warning statements.

An analysis of hazards of workplace tasks should be conducted to help establish proper and safe procedures. Jobs or tasks broken down into their steps are listed and the hazards involved in each step are identified. Finally, recommendations are made regarding how to best protect employees from these hazards or prevent them from occurring.

Create a manual containing information on every potentially hazardous drug or chemical. The manual can be organized alphabetically by generic name of the substance; each entry should contain both the MSDS (which explains the precautions that should be taken and first aid that should be performed in case of spill or exposure) and the product insert for the substance. You may wish to subdivide the manual into categories such as pesticides/topicals, oral medications, injectables, cleaning agents, and anesthetic agents.

Safety Equipment

General safety requirements include the routine use of protective equipment during certain procedures. Examples include:

♦ **Radiography**—Lead aprons, gloves, and neck guards
♦ **Bathing/Dipping**—Apron, safety goggles, and gloves
♦ **Dental procedures/surgery**—Goggles, face masks, gloves, and/or protective shields or barriers

AVMA Guide to Hazard Communication: JAVMA 196(2):Insert, 1990.

Some employees may be allergic to latex. An alternative type of glove should be available for their use.

Product Labeling

Each product must have a label that includes specific information about its ingredients, instructions on how to protect individuals from any dangers it poses, and first aid in the event of exposure to the product. If the substance is transferred to another container, a label with the same information must be placed on the new container.

Infectious Disease

Keep food and drink away from areas where animal products are used or stored. Use in separate refrigerators for medical supplies and food, and keep the coffee pot and microwave in a place other than the treatment rooms or the laboratory area.

Zoonoses

A zoonosis is a disease that may be transmitted from animals to humans. Zoonotic disease hazards vary with the type of practice and its location in the United States. Examples of zoonoses include:

♦ Toxoplasmosis (a hazard to pregnant women)
♦ Ringworm (a skin fungus)
♦ Roundworms

Familiarize yourself with the zoonotic diseases of concern in your area. Ensure that the hospital's safety program includes procedures to reduce risk of zoonotic disease transmission. Inform clients if their pet has a disease with zoonotic potential.

Hazardous Waste

An infectious waste management plan is required by state and/or federal law. Check with state authorities regarding specific regulations on proper disinfection/disposal of hazardous waste items. Examples of infectious waste include *Brucella abortus* vaccine vials or bodily fluids or organs from animals with zoonotic diseases. Sharps such as used needles and catheters are another type of hazardous waste. Immediately dispose of sharps in a puncture-proof container. Reusing needles increases the risk of injury to staff.

Equipment Safety

Any staff member using hospital equipment and supplies must be trained in their safe and proper use. For example, cylinders containing compressed gases should be stored away from potential heat sources, secured with a chain or strap, and have a protective cap in place when not in use.

Physical Hazards

A number of physical hazards may be encountered in practice, including:

♦ **Animal-related injuries**—Dog bites, cat scratches, and horse kicks are typical hazards in veterinary clinics. The hospital safety program should include training in restraint and handling of animals. Because a major cause of lawsuits is injury to clients attempting to restrain their own animals, only trained staff should perform restraint. Extremely aggressive animals should be tranquilized to avoid unnecessary risk to human handlers.

♦ **Falls**—Minimize slips and falls by adhering to a clear housekeeping plan, installing nonslip flooring, and wearing appropriate footwear.

♦ **Lifting injuries**—To minimize these types of injuries, store heavy items on the floor, use a dolly to transport heavy boxes, and use examination tables with an electronic lift feature for large dogs.

♦ **Hearing damage**—Hearing protection devices should be worn by anyone working in a kennel area longer than 15 minutes.

♦ **Fire**—Fire prevention and safety includes an evacuation plan, posting of appropriate emergency phone numbers, clear marking of exits, emergency lighting in the event of a power outage, and one-way locks on doors that will permit exit but not entry.

Reproductive Health Considerations

Health hazards of concern to women of child-bearing age include exposure to radiation, anesthetic gases, teratogenic or mutagenic chemicals, or zoonotic disease (some of these substances may harm the reproductive system in males as well). By following the recommendations above and/or reassigning duties of a pregnant staff member, exposure to these potential hazards will be minimized.

IF YOU ARE INJURED ON THE JOB

Injuries incurred as a result of employment in a veterinary hospital are covered by state worker's compensation laws. Most businesses are required to provide employees with worker's compensation insurance. This type of insurance is paid for entirely by your employer. Premiums are regulated by state law and vary according to the employee's classification. Premiums for a veterinarian or a technician are higher than those for a secretary or receptionist because the former are more likely to be injured on the job. Worker's compensation insurance covers all medical expenses and rehabilitation costs, disability income based on a percentage of wages, and a death benefit if the employee is killed on the job.

IF A CLIENT IS INJURED AT THE VETERINARY HOSPITAL

If a client is injured on the veterinary hospital's property (e.g., from tripping on a curb in the parking lot or slipping on a wet floor), the hospital's commercial general liability insurance policy should cover any medical expenses. The basic property and liability insurance might also cover the medical expenses of a client bitten by another client's pet in the hospital's waiting room. If an owner is injured while helping you restrain a horse for a treatment, however, he or she may have grounds for a malpractice suit.

BUILDING SECURITY

The location and design of the veterinary hospital are obvious factors that determine much of the building's potential security risk. Employees of established practices can do little to control these factors. However, common-sense precautions such as the following can help keep the building secure:

- ◆ Access for clients and other visitors to the building should be through the reception area only.
- ◆ Visitors should not be allowed to wander through the hospital unescorted.
- ◆ Doors to laboratories, examining rooms, and offices should be kept closed when not in use.
- ◆ Expensive laboratory and office equipment should be kept out of sight or at least away from windows.

Employees may be involved in the selection of such important security measures as lighting, locks, and alarm systems. Exterior lighting around the building and parking lot is essential not only for building security but also for the safety of clients and employees. Interior lights should be left on even when the hospital is closed as this will discourage burglars from breaking into the office.

Doors and window locks are an essential part of any security system; a locksmith should be consulted to determine the specific needs of your building. The condition of the doors and windows should be considered, as even the best locks will not be effective on flimsy or rotten doors or broken windows.

At least one room in the clinic can be designated as a "safe room"— a place where a staff member can go if he or she feels threatened, particularly when working alone. This room should have secure locks on any doors or windows and have a telephone available.

There are a number of alarm systems. For example, an alarm system may do one or more of the following:

- ◆ Emit a loud noise upon unauthorized entry into the building.
- ◆ Directly signal the police department.
- ◆ Trigger a central alarm system monitored by a private security company.

An alarm-only system is inexpensive but effective only if someone hears the alarm and calls the police. The latter two provide better security but entail a monthly maintenance or service charge in addition to the installation fee.

Once an alarm system has been installed, all employees should

PERSONAL SAFETY TIPS

♦ Have at least one arm free when walking.
♦ Keep the next key you need ready in your hand so that you can use it immediately when you get to your destination. The key can also be used as a weapon in emergencies.
♦ Park as close as you can to the building you are going to (under a street light, if possible, if you're arriving or know you may leave after dark).
♦ Stay alert and avoid potentially threatening situations.

become familiar with it so that it is used properly and effectively. For more information about alarm systems, contact your local police department or a private security firm.

Bibliography

Brody MD, Markland S: AVMA guide for veterinary medical waste management. *JAVMA* 195(4):440–452, 1989.

Guidelines for Hazards in the Workplace, in *AVMA Membership Directory and Resource Manual.* Schaumburg, IL, AVMA, 1997.

Job Hazard Analysis. OSHA Publication 3071–1985.

Health Hazards in Veterinary Practice, ed 3. Schaumburg, IL, AVMA, 1995.

Personal protective equipment—It's the law. AVMA Professional Liability Insurance Trust Safety Bulletin, vol 5, no 2, April 1997.

Zoonosis Updates. Schaumburg, IL, AVMA, 1990.

HUMAN EMERGENCIES AND FIRST AID

Innumerable emergencies—both medical and nonmedical—can occur in veterinary practice. Being prepared to handle any emergency will help you in the event that one actually occurs. Remaining calm will allow you to think more clearly and, perhaps, respond more efficiently. The basics of first aid are outlined below.

CALLING FOR HELP

Every emergency must be assessed; identify any condition that may be an immediate threat. When calling for help, be prepared to give the following information:

- Location of the emergency (including the names of cross streets, if possible)
- Telephone number from which the call is being made
- What happened
- How many persons need help
- Condition of the victim(s)
- What aid is being given to the victim(s)

Do not hang up until instructed to do so. The dispatcher may be able to give you instructions on how to care for the victim until help arrives.

FAINTING AND UNRESPONSIVENESS

Fainting is a partial or complete loss of consciousness that is caused by a temporary reduction of blood flow to the brain. It can be triggered by an emotional shock, specific medical conditions (e.g., heart disease), standing for long periods of time, overexertion, or pain.

Signs and Symptoms

Fainting may occur with or without warning. The victim may feel

IMPORTANT TELEPHONE NUMBERS

Medical Emergencies: Dial 911 or _____

Physician: _____

Ambulance: _____

Fire Department: _____

Paramedics/Rescue Squad: _____

Police

   Emergency: _____

   Nonemergency: _____

Utilities

   Gas: _____

   Electric: _____

   Water: _____

   Telephone Service: _____

Poison Hotline

   Human: _____

   Animal: ASPCA National Animal Poison Control Center
           1-800-548-2423 ($30/case) or 1-900-680-0000
           ($20/first 5 minutes plus 2.95/additional minute)

Trauma Center: _____

CHECKING THE ABCs

Checking the ABCs requires three steps:

♦ **A for Airway**—Be sure the victim has an open airway.

♦ **B for Breathing**—Look, listen, and feel for signs of breathing.

♦ **C for Circulation**—Check blood circulation (e.g., feel for pulse, look for severe bleeding).

---

light headed or dizzy, show signs of shock (e.g., skin is pale, cool, and moist) or nausea, or complain of numbness in fingers and toes.

First Aid

Persons who feel weak and dizzy should lie down with their feet elevated, or from a sitting position they should bend over so that their head is at the level of their knees.

Fainting victims usually recover spontaneously. Nonetheless, after a fainting attack has occurred:

♦ Determine if the victim is conscious; call for help. This is important to ensure the victim's recovery and to protect the practice from liability.

♦ Check the ABCs (see box above).

♦ Place the victim on his/her back.

♦ Elevate the victim's feet 8 to 12 inches.

♦ Loosen any tight clothing.

♦ If vomiting occurs, roll victim onto side or turn head to the side. This will allow vomitus to drain away, thus preventing aspiration. If necessary, wipe out the victim's mouth with your finger (gloves are recommended).

♦ If the victim fell, determine the extent of injury.

♦ **DO NOT** give the victim anything to eat or drink.

♦ **DO NOT** splash water on the victim's face; water can be aspirated and does little to stimulate the victim.

ANIMAL BITE WOUNDS

Bites and scratches from animals—especially dogs and cats—are common in veterinary hospitals and can result in open wounds. Although a dog bite is likely to cause more extensive tissue damage than a cat bite, the latter may be more dangerous because of the wider variety of bacteria usually present in the cat's mouth. Among the more serious concerns are rabies and tetanus. Any warm-blooded species can transmit rabies, and tetanus is a possible consequence of deep puncture wounds.

First Aid

♦ If the **wound is severe** and/or **bleeding is profuse**:
  —Try to control bleeding.
  —Seek medical attention immediately.
♦ If the **wound is minor**:
  —Control any bleeding.
  —Thoroughly flush and wash the wound with soap and water.
  —Apply an antibiotic ointment and a dressing, such as a sterile gauze pad. The dressing should extend at least 1 inch beyond the edge of the wound.
  —Watch for signs of infection.
  —Determine if there is a risk for rabies or tetanus.

LIFE-THREATENING EMERGENCIES

At least one person per working shift should be certified by the Red Cross in first aid, rescue breathing, and cardiopulmonary resuscitation (CPR). This person can deal with life-threatening emergencies such as stroke, heart attack, cessation of breathing, or choking.

If someone becomes unconscious, or falls and appears injured:

♦ **Immediately** designate one staff member to summon the emergency service (911, if available).
♦ Do not move the victim. If the spine is injured, moving could worsen the injury.
♦ Check the ABCs (see box on p. 104).
♦ Allow the staff member who is appropriately trained to perform first aid as necessary.

COURSES IN FIRST AID AND CPR

The American Red Cross provides consistent, reliable education and
(Text continues on p. 108)

VETERINARY HOSPITAL EMERGENCY POLICY

Every veterinary practice should have a protocol for each of the various types of emergencies that may occur. If your practice has not established such protocols, your initiative in developing them will eliminate confusion and ensure that appropriate measures are taken in times of crises.

Veterinary

_____

_____

_____

_____

_____

_____

_____

_____

Medical

_____

_____

_____

_____

_____

_____

_____

_____

_____

_____

Fire

_____

_____

_____

_____

_____

_____

_____

_____

_____

_____

Other

_____

_____

_____

_____

_____

_____

_____

_____

_____

_____

_____

_____

_____

BASIC FIRST AID KIT

♦ Sterile gauze pads (dressings), 2 and 4 inch squares for wounds
♦ Roller and triangular bandages for holding dressings in place and for making an arm sling
♦ Assorted sizes of adhesive bandages
♦ Scissors and tweezers
♦ Ice bag or chemical ice pack
♦ Disposable gloves
♦ Flashlight with extra batteries in a separate bag
♦ Antiseptic wipes

training in prevention and control of injury and illness. Basic and advanced courses are available for the general public and emergency care providers. Your local chapter of the Red Cross can provide information about the courses available in your area.

THE FIRST AID KIT

Every practice should have a first aid kit stocked and readily available. Contents of a standard kit are listed in the box above. To save time, preassembled kits can be purchased. The following points are important to observe:

♦ The size and contents of the kit should be suited to the practice. As human medical emergencies in a veterinary clinic are infrequent, a basic kit should suffice.
♦ The contents should be arranged so that every item can be found quickly.

Bibliography

The American National Red Cross: *First Aid: Responding to Emergencies,* ed 2. St Louis, Mosby–Year Book, 1996.

DRUG GUIDELINES

DISPENSING PRESCRIPTION DRUGS

Animal drugs approved by the FDA are classified as either veterinary prescriptions (R_x) or over-the-counter (OTC) drugs. Products classified as veterinary R_x are labeled "For use by or on the order of a licensed veterinarian." Statements like "For Veterinary Use Only" or "Sales to graduate veterinarians only" represent the manufacturer's or distributor's marketing policy and have no bearing on whether the product is an OTC or R_x animal drug.

Security precautions must be taken when dispensing prescription drugs. They are necessary to prevent theft, to ensure the safety of the animal for which the drug is prescribed, prevent violative drug residues in food-producing animals, and monitor the hospital pharmacy's inventory. A protocol for dispensing drugs should be established. Technicians may assist in dispensing prescription drugs under the supervision of a veterinarian and should become familiar with the routine in their hospital.

Prescription drugs must be used or prescribed only within the context of a valid veterinarian-client-patient relationship. Records should be maintained for at least 2 years (or more as mandated by law) for all such treatments or prescriptions. Your state may have regulations regarding who may perform the physical act of filling a prescription and writing its label after the doctor has written the order.

Once a protocol for dispensing drugs has been established, never deviate from it. Built-in safety checks should be a part of the routine. Any irregular requests should be questioned to avoid possible errors. If an order is not completely clear, ask for clarification. One routine is outlined here:

♦ Read (or hear) the order.
♦ Select the drug from the inventory; be sure to read the label.

♦ Consider the dose and quantity; if it seems inappropriate, question it.

♦ Pour or (in the case of pills) count the correct amount of drug into the dispensing container.

♦ Prepare and affix dispensing labels one at a time (see below).

♦ Check the final preparation.

♦ Return the stock drug to the shelf.

♦ Dispense the medication to the patient or client. If the drug is to be used at the owner's home, check the label and explain the procedure to the client.

The prescription label should include:

♦ Name, address, and phone number of the veterinarian

♦ Name, address, and phone number of the client

♦ Name of animal(s) being treated

♦ Date

♦ Name and quantity of the drug

♦ Dosage and directions for use (avoid abbreviations)

♦ Number of refills authorized

EXTRALABEL DRUG USE

Veterinarians may obtain and use drugs labeled for human use for the treatment of animal patients. They may also use and prescribe products labeled for animal use for medically appropriate clinical situations not stated on the drug's label. The Animal Medicinal Drug Use Clarification Act (AMDUCA) is a rule issued by the FDA to allow veterinarians to prescribe extralabel uses of certain drugs (approved for humans or other animals) for therapeutic purposes only.

Drugs used in an extralabel manner for animals are under the same restrictions as veterinary prescription drugs. This includes human medications such as pain relievers or PeptoBismol®. Contact the FDA at 301-594-1737 for more information.

DEA GUIDELINES

The Drug Enforcement Agency (DEA) regulates the distribution and use of controlled substances, which are divided into five schedules by their potential for abuse. All doctors who administer, prescribe, and dispense controlled substances must be registered with the DEA and renew their registration every 3 years.

The DEA requires that controlled substances be kept in a securely locked cabinet and meticulous records of their ordering, receipt, and use be maintained. All controlled substance records must be retained for 2 years. A veterinarian who dispenses or regularly administers controlled substances must take an inventory every 2 years of all stocks of the substances on hand. A minimum number of employees should have access to the controlled substance storage area. Any loss of controlled substances must be reported to the DEA and the local police department.

The DEA offers these guidelines for prescribers/dispensers of controlled substances:

♦ Prescription blanks should be kept in a safe place where they cannot be easily stolen. Only a small number of prescription pads should be in use at any one time.

♦ A separate prescription blank should be used for each controlled substance prescribed.

♦ Each veterinarian in the hospital should have his or her own personalized, prenumbered prescription blanks. If only institutional prescription blanks (i.e., with the name of the hospital imprinted rather than the name of the individual practitioner) are used, the veterinarian should print his or her name, address, and DEA registration number on the blank when writing a prescription.

♦ A typewriter or pen and ink should be used to complete prescription orders. An assistant may prepare the prescription and then have the veterinarian sign it.

♦ The actual amount of the prescription should be written out in addition to using an Arabic or Roman numeral; this will discourage attempts to alter prescription orders.

♦ Prescriptions should not be written for large quantities of controlled substances unless such quantities are definitely needed.

♦ Only a minimum stock of controlled substances should be maintained in the veterinary medical bag.

♦ The medical bag should not be left unattended in a vehicle. If necessary, the bag should be locked in the trunk.

♦ Prescription blanks should be used only for writing prescriptions and not for notes or memos. A drug abuser could easily erase the message and use the blank to forge an order for a prescription.

♦ The veterinarian should never sign prescription blanks in advance.

♦ Accurate records of the controlled substances dispensed must be kept.

♦ Phone the nearest DEA field office to obtain or furnish information. The call will be held in the strictest confidence.

DEA Domestic Field Offices are located throughout the country. The DEA Registration unit may be reached at 1-800-882-9539.

Bibliography

AVMA Membership Directory and Resource Manual. Schaumburg, IL, AVMA.
Compendium of Veterinary Products. North American Compendiums.
Veterinary Pharmaceuticals and Biologicals. Lenexa, KS, Veterinary Medicine Publishing Co.

REGULATORY AGENCIES

The veterinary industry is subject to the regulations of three departments of the federal government: the U.S. Department of Agriculture, the U.S. Department of Health and Human Services, and the U.S. Department of Justice. The functions of agencies within these departments that pertain to the veterinary field are summarized in this section.

U.S. DEPARTMENT OF AGRICULTURE (USDA)
Animal and Plant Health Inspection Service (APHIS)

The Veterinary Services Branch of APHIS is responsible for the prevention and eradication of animal diseases through a variety of programs. Regional offices are located throughout the United States; each office is directed by an Area Veterinarian in Charge (AVIC). Phone numbers and addresses are listed in the American Veterinary Medical Association's annual directory.

The agency has national programs in cattle diseases (e.g., brucellosis eradication), veterinary biologics, special diseases, technical assessment, and interstate inspection and compliance. The import-export staff oversees the movement of animals into this country to prevent the introduction of disease. The agency also acts in the event of animal disease emergencies. It administers the Animal Welfare Act and the Horse Protection Act, employing veterinarians and veterinary technicians as agents to inspect kennels, research facilities, and horse shows.

Food Safety Inspection Service (FSIS)

The function of FSIS is to ensure that all meat and poultry products sold in interstate commerce are safe, wholesome, and accurately and truthfully labeled. Its regional and area offices employ inspectors and veterinarians to conduct the inspections in accordance with federal regulations. Any product containing meat or poultry is subject to inspection by the agency.

Other Agencies

Other agencies within the USDA that deal with veterinary issues but are not strictly regulatory in nature are the Agricultural Research Service (ARS), the Extension Service, and the Cooperative State Research Service.

U.S. DEPARTMENT OF HEALTH AND HUMAN SERVICES

Food and Drug Administration (FDA)

The mission of the FDA is to ensure the safety and wholesomeness of foods and the safety and effectiveness of drugs and medical devices marketed in interstate commerce. Its main focus is on the final product that reaches the consumer, but all ingredients going into FDA-regulated products are also subject to the requirements of the Federal Food, Drug, and Cosmetic Act. The FDA's Center for Veterinary Medicine (CVM; see below) is responsible for ensuring the safety and effectiveness of animal drugs and feeds. Drugs and additives intended for use in food-producing animals are also evaluated for human health concerns (i.e., for residues that may remain in meat, milk, or eggs). In cases in which violative residues are found, the FDA is responsible for determining the cause and to take appropriate regulatory action.

Other agencies such as the USDA and Environmental Protection Agency (EPA) also have responsibilities associated with food animals. The FDA is responsible for food animals on the farm, the USDA assumes responsibility for animal processing at the meat-packing plant, and the FDA resumes its regulatory role when processed products are in the marketplace. The EPA evaluates and establishes residue tolerances for pesticides applied to ingredients used in feed for food-producing animals. The FDA assumes regulatory follow-up if violative residues are found in meat, milk, or eggs.

Center for Veterinary Medicine (CVM)

The CVM is the branch of the FDA that regulates the manufacture and distribution of drugs and feed additives intended for animals. The CVM staff evaluates new animal drug applications (NADAs) and grants approval for products that are determined to be safe and effective. In addition, its Surveillance and Compliance Divisions monitor the animal health industry (by means of field inspections) for violations of good manufacturing processes (of veterinary drugs) and for the use of unapproved and illegal drugs, the diversion of prescription drugs, and extralabel use of drugs in species for which the drug is not approved.

Other Agencies

Other agencies within the Department of Health and Human Services include the Centers for Disease Control (CDC), the National Institutes of Health (NIH), and the Public Health Service (PHS).

U.S. DEPARTMENT OF JUSTICE
Drug Enforcement Administration (DEA)

The DEA's function is to control narcotic and dangerous drug abuse through law enforcement and prevention. The DEA cooperates with other federal agencies as well as state and local governments, private industry, and other organizations. The DEA has district, division, and resident offices across the country. For more information on the DEA, see p. 110.

ENVIRONMENTAL PROTECTION AGENCY (EPA)

The EPA is an independent federal agency whose Office of Pesticide Programs and Office of Enforcement regulate the use of pesticides in veterinary practice. The Federal Insecticide, Fungicide, and Rodenticide Act (FIFRA), which regulates pesticide use, is administered by the USDA, but the EPA has the power to excuse veterinarians from meeting some of its requirements if specific safety precautions are followed. As mentioned earlier, the EPA also evaluates and establishes residue tolerances for pesticides applied to ingredients used in feed for food-producing animals. The EPA does not address the issue of pesticide safety for animals. Its focus is on residues that could affect the environment or human health.

ASSOCIATION OF AMERICAN FEED CONTROL OFFICIALS (AAFCO)

AAFCO provides an organization through which officials can unite to explore the problems of administering laws regulating the production, labeling, distribution, and sale of animal feeds and livestock remedies. It also develops uniform definitions for all feed ingredients and drafts uniform wording for regulations and bills that can be enacted by each jurisdiction. AAFCO publishes a handbook of definitions, rules, and regulations annually.

TRAVELING WITH PETS

Clients may ask the veterinary technician for advice on traveling with their pets. Many animals do not travel well, especially those that are ill or excitable, and in some cases it may be better to leave the pet with trusted friends or relatives or at a reputable boarding kennel or hire a responsible pet sitter.

If the decision is made to travel, however, it is essential for pet owners to begin planning well in advance of the trip. It is important for them to check in advance with hotels and other accommodations to ensure that the pet will be welcome. Preparation is particularly important when traveling internationally because of the many and varied requirements for animal entry into foreign countries.

No matter what the mode of travel, the animal should have a collar with an identificatin tag. Additional requirements for interstate or foreign travel are outlined below.

TRAVELING BY CAR

If clients are planning to travel by car, suggest that they take their pet for several short rides to accustom it to riding in a car. An animal should be restrained in a pet seat belt or ride in a carrying cage. A pet should not be allowed to ride with its head out the window; wind and debris can injure the animal's eyes, nose, and ears or it may suddenly jump out the window. Animals are prone to motion sickness and thus should not be fed for a few hours before traveling. The veterinarian can also prescribe an antinausea medication or tranquilizers.

The owner should bring a supply of the pet's regular food (preferably dry, for convenience; if canned food is fed, throw out the unused portion if it cannot be refrigerated). It is important to bring along an ample supply of drinking water as well. Owners should stop every 2 hours and exercise their pet on a leash.

If the pet must be left in a parked car for a short time, all the doors

117

should be locked (to prevent theft) and the windows left open just enough to provide ventilation but not to allow the animal to jump out or get its head caught. A pet should never be left in a car in hot or humid weather; heat prostration and even death can occur in a very short time, sometimes within minutes. The car must be parked in shade.

TRAVELING BY AIRPLANE

When traveling by commercial airline, it is important to contact the airline well in advance of the departure date to make reservations and to find out if there are any special regulations. Current health and rabies vaccination certificates are required.

Some airlines allow a small pet in carrying cases to travel with its owner in the passenger compartment. It is important that clients check with the airline on its limitations and reserve space early if they wish to take their pet in the cabin with them. Often, however, an animal must be shipped in the baggage compartment. If possible, suggest that the client try to book a nonstop, midweek flight during off-peak hours so that the pet will be more likely to receive adequate attention from airline personnel. In hot weather the risk of overheating can be reduced by taking an early morning or late evening flight.

The client should plan to arrive at the airport early to allow time to exercise the animal and get it situated in its cage. Most airlines have strict requirements with regard to the dimensions and construction of animal shipping crates; therefore the client should check with the airline in advance and, if necessary, arrange to purchase an appropriate crate. The cage should allow enough room for the animal to stand, turn, and lie down, and it should have a leakproof bottom. Ventilation holes on opposite sides of the cage should have rims or protrusions on the outside to prevent blockage of air flow. The cage should be labeled "Live Animal" and the upright position clearly marked with arrows. The pet's name, the owner's name, the address and phone number of the owner's home and of the final destination, and any special instructions should be indicated on both the outside and inside of the crate and on a tag attached to the pet's collar. Each crate must have a funnel, a tube, and a pan so the dog or cat may safely be given water. It should also have absorbent bedding that will prevent the animal from getting wet. A piece of clothing with the owner's scent may also help give the pet a sense of security.

THE HEALTH CERTIFICATE

All states require a health certificate issued by an accredited, practicing veterinarian if an animal is to be shipped across state lines. This requirement applies to livestock, poultry, and horses as well as pet animals. The veterinarian must certify that he or she has inspected the animal(s) and that it is not showing signs of any infectious, contagious, and/or communicable diseases. Vaccinations and test results are also recorded on the certificate. There are four copies of the certificate: one for the issuing veterinarian's files, one for the animal's owner or shipper, and two copies to be sent to the State Veterinarian in the state of origin (at the Division of Animal Health in the state's Department of Agriculture, which administers the program in cooperation with the U.S. Department of Agriculture's Animal and Plant Health Inspection Service). The State Veterinarian endorses one copy, certifying that the issuing veterinarian is accredited and licensed to practice in the state of origin and mails it to the State Veterinarian in the destination state; the other copy is filed at the state of origin. Preprinted certificates are available from the State Veterinarian. A veterinary hospital may have its own certificates printed, which include its name and logo, but key wording must be the same. For more information, contact your State Veterinarian.

TRAVEL TO ANOTHER STATE

Requirements for transport of dogs and cats from one state to another vary, but almost all states require a rabies vaccination certificate for dogs (only a few states require them for cats) and a health certificate issued by an accredited practicing veterinarian. The State Veterinarian or chief animal health official in the state of destination should be contacted for current information.

TRAVEL TO A FOREIGN COUNTRY

The many regulations governing travel with or shipment of dogs and cats to foreign countries vary widely from country to country and are subject to change. The client should obtain current information from the embassy of the country of destination or from one of that country's consular offices (located in most major U.S. cities). In addition, international airports may have information on regulations in the countries they serve.

Requirements can include a quarantine period, vaccinations (within acceptable time limits), and special documents (health certificates, vaccination certificates, and import licenses). In most countries the pet owner is responsible for making arrangements for boarding the animal during quarantine.

For travel to Canada, the owner must show a health certificate signed by a licensed veterinarian (U.S. or Canadian) that the pet has been vaccinated against rabies within the past 12 months.

It is important to tell clients to complete all paperwork before traveling to avoid unpleasant incidents and, at worst, the possibility that their pet could be destroyed at the airport in some countries if the required procedures have not been followed.

The reentry of pets into the United States from foreign countries is regulated by the Public Health Service.

CANINE CARE

CANINE DATA CHART

Life span	8–20+ years, depending on breed
Normal body temperature	100°–102°F (37.7°–38.8°C)
Respiration	10–30 breaths per minute
Pulse	Adults: 70–160 per minute Toy breeds: 70–180 per minute Puppies: 80–220 per minute
Blood collection sites	Cephalic vein, jugular vein, recurrent tarsal vein
Normal hemogram values	Hematocrit: 38%–55% White blood cells: 5,000–17,000/cu mm Total protein: 5.5–7.7 g/dl
Breeding information	
• **Puberty**	6–18 months of age, depending on breed
• **Breeding season**	Every 6–9 months, often in spring and fall
• **Gestation**	57–69 days (avg. 63); puppies are palpable from day 18–24 and 55–63, visible via ultrasound after day 28, and visible via radiography after day 43
• **Litter size**	1–8 puppies
• **Signs of heat**	Swollen vulva and blood-tinged vaginal discharge for 7–10 days, followed by a clear serous discharge for 4–7 days when the bitch attracts and accepts male dogs; phase of cycle may be determined by vaginal cytology
Neonates	Eyes open and ears functional at 10–17 days of age Puppies weaned at 6–8 weeks of age
Sexing	Males have a pendulous penis and suspended testes; testes may not be apparent at birth

BATHING

Bathing once a month will suffice unless the dog has a skin problem that requires more frequent attention. Dogs should be bathed before they are dipped for fleas and ticks. Take care that young puppies do not become chilled. If a blow dryer is used, keep it at the lowest setting to avoid burns.

Protective Gear

A shaking dog can splash shampoo or dip into unprotected eyes, and many pesticides may be absorbed through the skin. There are risks of both short-term and long-term exposure to pesticide dips and shampoos. Always wear a waterproof apron, gloves, and goggles to protect yourself.

Procedure

Preparation

♦ Find an area large enough to accommodate the dog. (Large dogs may be happier being bathed outside, weather permitting.)
♦ Cover the floor of the bathing area with a nonskid mat for traction.
♦ Comb any mats and burrs out of the hair coat.
♦ For male dogs, coat the scrotal skin with petrolatum jelly (some therapeutic shampoos may be irritating to sensitive skin).
♦ Place cotton in the dog's ears and protective ointment in its eyes before bathing or dipping.

Baths

♦ Begin the bathing procedure at the dog's nose and work back toward the tail (to prevent fleas from running to the dog's head).
♦ Use a sponge to clean the face, head, and ears.
♦ Shampoo tips:
   —Small amounts of shampoo go a long way; too much will be difficult to rinse off.
   —Shampoo lathers better if the measured amount is diluted with water before application.
   —Most therapeutic shampoos must be left on the hair for at least 10 minutes before rinsing.
♦ Make sure you rinse the dog thoroughly. Rinse until you think all the soap is out, and then rinse one more time.

Dips
- ◆ For dips supplied as concentrations, carefully follow label instructions regarding dilution.
- ◆ Pour and sponge the dip solution over the dog so that every part of the body is covered.
- ◆ Allow the dip to dry completely on the dog.

REPRODUCTION
Contraception
The most common methods of contraception are ovariohysterectomy (spaying) in female dogs and vasectomy or castration in males. These surgical procedures are permanent and irreversible (see Surgery, p. 131).

There is no need for a bitch to go through a first heat or to have a litter before being spayed. In fact, the risk of mammary tumors is greatly reduced in bitches that are spayed before their first heat.

There are several medications on the market that can be given to female dogs to render them temporarily infertile. The effectiveness of these products varies with the product, the phase of the reproductive cycle during which it is given, and individual response.

Clients should be advised that chemical termination of a pregnancy is not without risk. Potentially terminal bleeding and/or uterine infection might result.

Breeding
Reproductive efficiency is greatest between 3 and 5 years of age. Bitches should not be bred on the first heat because they have not yet achieved their full growth. The heat period may last 21 to 28 days; the bitch is usually receptive to the male between days 4 through 14 of the cycle, but the length of the receptive period can vary widely.

Whelping
Late in gestation the bitch requires increased amounts of a well-balanced, high-energy diet to meet the needs of the developing offspring as well as to enable the bitch to produce enough milk for the offspring (see Diet and Feeding, p. 141). Lactation may begin as early as 7 days prepartum in the pregnant bitch, but most females produce milk 48

hours before they whelp. The bitch's appetite may decrease and nest building behavior begins 24 to 36 hours before parturition. A reduction in the bitch's body temperature of about 1.1°F signifies that whelping is 12 to 24 hours away. A whelping box should be provided in a quiet, dimly lit area that is free of drafts. The bitch should be left alone in the whelping box with free access to food and clean water and should be monitored as unobtrusively as possible.

If a puppy is not born within 2 hours of the start of abdominal contractions (true labor), the bitch may need medical attention. Once the bitch successfully expels a puppy, it should remove the translucent sac from the puppy within 2 minutes of birth (if it does not, the person in attendance should be prepared to do so to prevent the puppy from suffocating). After removing the membrane, the bitch will lick the puppy briskly, drying it and stimulating respiration. If the bitch does not bite through the umbilical cord to separate the puppy from the placenta, the cord can be tied off with clean suture or cotton umbilical tape ½ inch from the navel. The remaining cord is cut off with scissors. If the dam does not deliver another puppy within 30 minutes of giving birth and is obviously still in labor, it should be examined by a veterinarian for a fetal obstruction or for partial uterine inertia. It is important to count the placentas; there should be one for each puppy after whelping is completed. The bitch should not be allowed to eat more than one or two placentas because they will cause gastrointestinal upset. A greenish discharge will normally drain from the vulva for up to 12 hours immediately postpartum; this discharge will be replaced by a dark red to brownish discharge, which may last from 2 to 4 weeks.

Some of the complications of whelping include dystocia (the inability to expel a puppy while in labor), retained placentas, mastitis, uterine infections, and eclampsia (attributed to calcium deficiency). Cannibalism, or the savaging of puppies, is sometimes seen in young dams. This problem is usually alleviated by sedating the dam until it becomes accustomed to the puppies.

Pseudopregnancies are common in bitches and are thought to be caused by the endogenous production of a pituitary hormone. Clinical signs include abdominal distention, nesting behavior, and mammary enlargement with subsequent lactation for periods of up to 2 weeks. Signs will normally be present at about 60 days postovulation and regress 1 or 2 weeks later. Ovariohysterectomy (spaying) is the only known method of preventing pseudopregnancies; however, ovariohysterectomy during pseudopregnancy can prolong the clinical signs.

PUPPY CARE
Neonatal Development

For all practical purposes newborn puppies are completely helpless. They rely on the lactating bitch for warmth, food, and cleanliness. They are incapable of thermal regulation for the first 6 days of life and require an external heat source for their first 3 weeks. They nurse every 1 to 2 hours for the first week; the bitch licks their external genitalia both to stimulate urination and defecation and to clean them after every feeding. Between 5 to 17 days after whelping the puppies' eyes open, but they have limited vision; a day or so later their ear canals open. By 18 days of age they begin to move around and explore their environment.

Nursing and Weaning

As mentioned, newborn puppies nurse every 1 to 2 hours for the first week. The sucking reflex is initiated within minutes of birth so that the puppies can consume colostrum, which contains antibodies to protect them from infectious diseases. If puppies are restless and crying, they probably are not getting enough milk to drink, and supplementation with a formula should be considered (see Orphan Formulas, p. 126). Peak lactation will occur between 3 and 6 weeks postpartum.

Puppies are usually weaned at 6 weeks of age. Many bitches begin weaning their puppies as early as 4 weeks after whelping. A soft, readily digestible gruel should be introduced to the puppies' diet as early as 3 to 4 weeks after birth so they will become accustomed to consuming solid food before weaning occurs.

Housing

Puppies should be kept in a small box with sides high enough to keep them inside the box and to prevent drafts. The bottom of the box should be raised off the floor and covered with a disposable or washable flooring with padding (such as with indoor-outdoor carpeting and disposable diapers or cotton towels) to keep the puppies as warm and dry as possible. Materials that become slippery when wet, such as newspapers, should not be used as bedding. Covered hot water bottles or heating pads set on the lowest setting (never higher—severe burns can result) may help keep the environmental temperature stable. Do not cover the entire floor with a heating pad; the puppy must be able to get away from the heat source if it gets too warm. A puppy's body temperature should be maintained at 96° to 97°F the first week of life and at 97° to 100°F the second, third, and fourth weeks. A ticking clock placed in the box may help to keep puppies quiet.

Nutrition

If puppies are fed properly, they should gain 5% to 10% of their birth weights daily and double their birth weight. Overfeeding should be avoided as it may cause obesity and skeletal diseases. It is important to remember that puppies require twice the fat and protein and more calcium and phosphorus than ordinary cow's milk can provide. Specific feeding instructions can be found in the Diet and Feeding section (p. 141).

Orphan Puppies

Hand-raising orphan puppies requires a great deal of time and effort. The ideal solution to the problem of caring for a motherless puppy is to locate a lactating bitch that will accept the puppy and raise it with its own. When a foster bitch is not available, it is necessary to hand-feed the puppy until about 4 to 6 weeks of age. However, the puppy should be left with any littermates between feedings so it can interact with them and learn appropriate social behavior. Puppies are usually mature enough to be sold between 6 and 8 weeks of age.

Orphan Formulas

One of the following can be used as an orphan formula for puppies:

♦ Commercial bitch's milk substitutes (powdered or liquid)— Follow manufacturer's instructions for preparation.
♦ One part dry puppy food to three parts water—Process in a blender.
♦ Two parts canned puppy food to one part water—Process in a blender.

AMOUNT OF FORMULA TO FEED PER DAY

Week of life	Amount per 100 g body weight
1	13 ml
2	17 ml
3	20 ml
4	22 ml

None of these choices is a perfect substitute for the bitch's milk, however.

Methods of Feeding

Although puppies can be fed with a baby bottle (using a premature infant's nipple), the quickest and most efficient method is tube feeding. Measure the distance between the tip of the nose and the last rib and mark this point on a feeding tube (size 8 to 10 French) or soft male urethral catheter. With the puppy held in a normal position, slowly insert the feeding tube into the mouth and pass it to the distance marked on the tube. (This measurement should be changed on the tube weekly as the puppy grows.) If the tube will not pass, it is probably in the trachea and should be rerouted. Warmed formula should be slowly injected into the feeding tube via a syringe from which all air has been expelled. If regurgitation occurs, no more should be fed until the next scheduled feeding. Puppies should be fed four times a day.

After each feeding the puppy should be cleaned and the anal-genital areas should be swabbed with moist cotton to stimulate urination and defecation.

When the puppy reaches 3 to 4 weeks of age, a soft gruel of commercial puppy food and water blended together should be offered several times daily (refer to the Diet and Feeding section, p. 141). The puppy should be weaned by 6 weeks of age or sooner if it is consuming adequate amounts of commercial puppy food.

PREVENTIVE HEALTH SCHEDULE

Puppies should be checked for gastrointestinal parasites at 3 weeks of age, and they require fecal rechecks when they return for their vaccinations. Heartworm preventive medication should be started at 6 to 8 weeks of age in areas where heartworm is endemic. The initial vaccination series consists of one injection of a combined vaccine (multivalent) given at 6 to 8 weeks of age or about 2 weeks after weaning. Boosters are given twice at 4 week intervals (see Vaccinations, p. 133). Puppies whose immune status is uncertain may receive an additional injection of combined vaccine as early as 2 weeks of age. In most states the rabies vaccine is given at 3 months of age.

House-Training

By instinct a dog will not soil its bed if given alternative areas on which to relieve itself. During the first 3 weeks of the puppies' life the bitch licks the external genitalia every few hours with its tongue to stimulate urination and defecation and to clean the puppies. The bitch ingests the excreted waste, which would otherwise soil the bedding. Once puppies are old enough to begin eating solid food, they wander a short distance away from the nest to relieve themselves.

Puppies are not capable of controlling urination or defecation until 8 weeks of age. Before this time they express their bowels or bladder 15 to 30 minutes after waking and eating, during intense activity, and before bedtime. House-training a new puppy usually takes 2 to 4 weeks and is accomplished through confinement, a regular schedule of feeding and elimination breaks, and a great deal of praise but no punishment.

Initially, the puppy should be confined to a small box or crate that is large enough for it to lie down in with its legs extended. Food should be offered on a regular schedule (see Diet and Feeding, p. 141). Every hour and before bedtime the animal should be carried to a designated area to relieve itself. Successful urination or defecation should be rewarded with lavish praise. Food or large amounts of water should not be left in the crate with the puppy overnight.

The length of time between trips to relieve itself can be extended as the puppy learns to control its bladder and bowels. The puppy will signal its intent by crying or sniffing earnestly at the floor. The area of confinement should be gradually enlarged as the puppy learns control until it can spend the day unconfined. Nonetheless, even when completely house-trained, puppies should be confined to small areas at night to prevent accidents from occurring.

DETERMINING A PUPPY'S AGE BY DENTITION

Teeth	Age at Which Teeth Appear
Deciduous incisors	2–6 weeks
Full deciduous dentition[a]	8 weeks
Permanent incisors	4–5 months
Permanent premolars	4–6 months
Permanent canines	5–6 months
Full permanent dentition[b]	6–10 months

[a]Full deciduous dentition:
    Maxillary teeth—6 incisors, 2 canines, 6 premolars
    Mandibular teeth—6 incisors, 2 canines, 6 premolars
[b]Full permanent dentition
    Maxillary teeth—6 incisors, 2 canines, 8 premolars, 4 molars
    Mandibular teeth—6 incisors, 2 canines, 8 premolars, 6 molars

DENTAL CARE*
Normal Dentition

A tooth consists of a core of dentin covered with enamel at the crown and cementum at the root. At the center of a tooth is a bundle of epithelial tissues made up of nerves and blood vessels (the dental pulp). Dogs have four types of teeth: incisors, canines, premolars, and molars. Each tooth performs a different role (tearing, shearing, or grinding) in mastication.

Dogs are diphyodont animals; they produce a generation of deciduous teeth that are shed and replaced by permanent teeth when the jaw reaches its mature size. Deciduous incisors appear as early as 2 weeks of age. Full dentition is usually present by 8 weeks of age. Shortly after the deciduous tooth is completely erupted, it starts to undergo an absorptive process beginning at the root. Under each deciduous tooth root a permanent tooth bud starts to develop. The deciduous tooth is shed when the permanent tooth erupts through the gums (gingiva). Permanent teeth erupt a few days earlier in large breed dogs than in smaller breeds.

Typically, a dog has a scissors bite. A scissors bite is characterized by a slight overlap of the maxillary (upper) incisors over the mandibu-

*More details about canine dental care are provided in Waltham Basic Canine Dentistry, a video/manual package for veterinary hospital staff that can be purchased by calling 1-888-371-7900.

lar (lower) incisors and an interdigitation of the mandibular canine teeth with the maxillary canines and corner incisors.

Recognizing Dental Problems

Jaw Abnormalities

The major inherited defects of the jaw are brachygnathism, in which the maxilla protrudes beyond the mandible, and prognathism, where the mandible protrudes beyond the maxilla. Prognathism is considered a normal trait in brachycephalic breeds such as boxers, English bulldogs, and Boston bull terriers. Animals affected with brachygnathism should not be used for breeding purposes.

Supernumerary Teeth

A normal adult dog with full dentition has 42 teeth. Extra permanent teeth, usually premolars, are commonly found in some breeds, such as spaniels, hounds, and greyhounds. These teeth should be removed as soon as possible to avoid tooth crowding and resultant malocclusion.

Retained Deciduous Teeth

Retained teeth are commonly found in toy breeds. The teeth that most often fail to be shed are incisors and canine teeth. Permanent malocclusion and possible trauma to the hard palate will occur if these teeth are not removed.

Tooth Abnormalities

Tooth abnormalities seen in dogs include tetracycline or antibiotic staining, enamel hypoplasia, caries, and periodontal disease.

Routine Cleaning

Dogs should have their teeth examined and, if necessary, professionally cleaned at least once a year. Some dogs, especially toy breeds on moist diets, require cleaning twice a year. Teeth cleaning is necessary to remove plaque and dental calculus that accumulate on the teeth at the gum line and cause gum inflammation (gingivitis) and periodontal disease.

A mask should be worn by the technician cleaning the teeth to prevent the inhalation of aerosolized bacteria. The procedure is as follows:

♦ Following an overnight fast, the dog is anesthetized and intubated.

♦ Position the dog's head so that its nose is pointing downward slightly to allow fluids to drain from the mouth.

♦ Place cotton towels under the head to soak up water and keep the dog's head dry.

♦ Remove large deposits of calculus with dental hand scalers.

♦ Thoroughly clean the teeth with hand scalers (a time-consuming method) or a mechanical (ultrasonic or rotating) scaler. Take care not to traumatize sensitive gum tissue or scratch the enamel surface of the tooth.

♦ Check the depth of the periodontal pockets for evidence of periodontal disease and note any suspicious areas that may harbor dental caries.

♦ Polish the teeth with pumice to remove minute scratches in the enamel, which may become sites for plaque accumulation.

Home Care

Owners can lightly brush their dog's teeth at least twice a week to remove plaque deposits. A child's nylon toothbrush dipped in a toothpaste made for dogs should be used. Do not use toothpastes made for humans, which can cause nausea in dogs if swallowed. Also, baking soda and/or salt should never be used to brush a pet's teeth. Many pets that need daily toothbrushing may have or be predisposed to heart disease and the extra sodium could have life-threatening effects.

If the dog will not tolerate a toothbrush, the owner can try using a soft cloth instead. Dog biscuits, hard objects to chew on, and dry dog food also help prevent dental plaque accumulation.

SURGERY
Spaying (Ovariohysterectomy)

Spaying is an irreversible means by which a female dog is rendered sterile. The procedure entails complete removal of the uterus and ovaries, thereby eliminating the estrous cycle. Once spayed, females no longer attract males.

Surgery is preceded by a fasting period and requires general anesthesia and hospitalization for a full day. Complications are unusual but may include postsurgical hemorrhage, uterine stump infection, tissue reaction to ligature material, and urinary incontinence. Because there is a greater risk of hemorrhage in bitches that are in heat or pregnant, these dogs are not usually spayed.

Postoperative care includes restriction of exercise for a week, protection of the incision from contaminants, and daily monitoring of the incision for inflammation or discharge. The incision must stay dry (i.e., no bathing or swimming until the sutures are removed). Suture removal is usually performed 7 to 10 days after surgery. Weight gains of up to 25% can occur following spaying if the bitch is allowed to be sedentary and overeat.

Castration (Orchiectomy)

Castration entails the surgical removal of both testes and renders the male dog irreversibly sterile. The procedure can be performed as early as 6 weeks of age and requires general anesthesia preceded by a fasting period. The dog can usually return home the afternoon of the surgery if there are no complications (which include scrotal bruising and swelling, postsurgical hemorrhage, and infection). Postoperative care includes restriction of exercise for a few days and protection of the incision from contaminants such as dirt, saliva, and water. The sutures are removed 7 to 10 days after surgery. Sexual activity usually declines within 6 months of castration. Other postoperative changes include weight gains and decreased incidences of aggression, roaming, and urine marking.

Ear Cropping (Cosmetic Otoplasty)

Ear trimming does not need to be performed except on the owner's request. The procedure should be done only in puppies that are healthy and well nourished to minimize the possibility of infection. Requirements vary with breed and are based on standards of the American Kennel Club. The age at which the procedure is best performed ranges from 8 to 24 weeks, depending on the breed. Success rates decrease with age.

The surgery is performed under general anesthesia, preceded by a fasting period. Complications include infection, unsightly blemishes, otitis externa, medial or lateral deviation of the tip of the ears, and failure of the ears to stand.

The puppy is sent home with its ears bandaged and will feel pain for about 5 days after surgery. The bandages must be checked daily for malpositioning, odors, and exudates. The sutures are removed 7 to 10 days after surgery. The ears must be checked and rebandaged regularly for 4 to 6 weeks. External support of the ear may be required for as long as 20 weeks.

Dewclaw Removal

The best time to remove dewclaws is when the puppy is 2 to 3 days old. Because the blood supply to the affected toe is minimal, the appendage can be quickly snipped off with sharp, clean scissors. Suturing with an absorbable material is preferred. A tiny tape bandage can be placed over the wound. If dewclaw removal is performed at 3 to 5 days of age, absorbable suture or tissue adhesive is required.

In older dogs dewclaw removal is more involved and requires general anesthesia and routine surgical preparation. Postoperative care is limited to keeping the bandage clean and dry for the 3 days it must be worn. Sutures can be removed 7 to 10 days after surgery.

Tail Docking

Ideally, tails should be surgically shortened during the first 5 days of life when the blood supply to the tail is minimal. The procedure does not need to be performed except at the owner's request. Tail length requirements vary with the breed of dog and are based on official standards of the American Kennel Club. Anesthesia is not required for the procedure. A single suture is placed to pull the skin edges together over the amputated stump; hemorrhage is minimal. The suture remains in place until it is removed by the dog.

Tail amputation in older dogs is an involved procedure that requires an overnight fast, general anesthesia, and adequate hemostasis. Postoperative complications include hemorrhage, infection, and a hairless scar.

VACCINATIONS

Dogs are very susceptible to certain infectious diseases, especially canine distemper, infectious canine hepatitis, parvovirus, parainfluenza, leptospirosis, and rabies. Colostrum in the bitch's milk contains antibodies, which usually protect them from these diseases for 6 to 8 weeks. Once the puppies lose this maternal antibody protection, they are at high risk of contracting the aforementioned diseases if exposed to an infected animal. Because the duration of protection provided by maternal antibody varies from animal to animal, vaccines should be given regularly until the pup is 16 to 22 weeks of age. Vaccinating at more frequent intervals than the label recommends is not helpful and could be harmful:

♦ Antibodies produced from each vaccination persist in the bloodstream for several weeks; any antigen (vaccine) introduced while maternal antibody is still present will be tied up by that antibody. Thus an adequate immune response will not result.

♦ Overvaccinating could induce an allergic reaction.

Once the vaccination series is completed, boosters should be given according to the vaccine manufacturer's recommendation.

Although most dogs are protected by the vaccinations when administered appropriately, immune deficiencies in some of these animals may prevent them from mounting adequate antibody responses.

PARASITES
Fleas and Ticks
Flea Life Cycle

Knowledge of the life cycle of the flea is a tremendous aid in the battle against this ubiquitous parasite. When environmental conditions are favorable, the flea has great reproductive potential. Fleas thrive at low altitudes at temperatures of 65° to 80°F. Under these conditions the flea life cycle can be completed in as little as 12 to 14 days.

The female flea lays her eggs in the hair coat of the animal. Because the eggs are not sticky, they tend to fall off the animal into areas where the dog sleeps or plays. The eggs then hatch into very small, worm-like larvae. The larvae feed on organic debris, especially the dried blood droppings (flea dirt) left by adult fleas. The larvae molt and spin cocoons to form pupae that usually emerge as young, hungry adults in about 3 weeks; under certain conditions, however, the pupae can remain dormant for nearly a year.

CANINE VACCINATION PROTOCOLS

Vaccine	Initial Administration (Weeks of Age)	Booster	Recommendations
Distemper virus	8, 12, and 16	Annual	Recommended for all dogs
Measles virus	6–8 (one dose) followed by distemper vaccine 2–4 weeks later	None	Optional; not for dogs over 12 weeks of age
Adenovirus-2	8, 12, and 16	Annual	Recommended for all dogs
Parainfluenza (injectable)	8, 12, and 16	Annual	Recommended for all dogs
Parvovirus (MLV)	8, 12, and 16	Annual	Recommended for all dogs
Coronavirus	9 and 12	Annual	Optional; of uncertain value
Leptospira	12 and 16 Not recommended in puppies <12 weeks old	Annual	Recommended; may not protect for more than 6–8 months
Bordetella bronchiseptica (injectable)	9 and 12	Annual	Recommended for dogs in contact with others during boarding, travel, training, or work
Bordetella/ Parainfluenza (intranasal)	As early as 3 weeks	Annual or 1 week prior to group exposure	Same as for injectable *Bordetella*
Borrelia burgdorferi	12 and 15	Annual	Optional; limited application
Rabies virus	12 or 16 Actual age may be established by local statutes	Every 1 to 3 years as required by state or local law	Required; does not meet legal requirements if administered by unauthorized person

Once emerged, an adult flea can live about 2 weeks before taking a blood meal from a host. Once it begins feeding, it must continue to feed regularly or it will die. Adult females begin laying eggs within 1 to 2 days of feeding.

Fleas can be hard to find on a dog. However, they often produce evidence of their presence in the form of "flea dirt" and/or scratching on the part of the dog. Flea dirt can be seen on the dog even when fleas are not readily visible. After combing or brushing a flea-infested dog, tiny dark dots or comma-shaped pieces of debris will be found. If these particles are combed onto a piece of wet white paper, they will dissolve and stain the paper red (the flea dirt is partially digested blood).

Tick Life Cycle

Ticks lay their eggs (as many as 18,000 in some species) in sheltered areas on or near the ground. Seed ticks hatch from the eggs and climb onto grass to wait for a suitable host. Once on a dog, they attach themselves to the skin and feed on blood, causing painful nodules wherever they attach.

Flea and Tick Control

Control on the Animal

Successful control of fleas and ticks depends on eliminating these pests from the dog and the environment. To control fleas on a dog, all animals in the household must be part of the flea control program.

Flea control products for adult dogs include a variety of drugs and chemicals available as collars, shampoos, sprays, dips, powders, long-lasting topicals, and oral medications. There are two basic categories of flea control products:

◆ Adulticides—These products kill adult fleas.
◆ Insect growth regulators (IGRs)/insect development inhibitors (IDIs)—These products prevent fleas from hatching or maturing.

The veterinarian will choose a product or products that combine safety, efficacy, and ease of use for the client. Often a combination of adulticide and an IGR or IDI is used.

Environmental Control

A complete flea and tick control program also includes a thorough treatment of the pet's environment. Places where dogs spend most of their time will have the greatest numbers of deposited eggs and newly emerged adult fleas and ticks. Thorough cleaning of the house and yard should precede any application of insecticides. It is always best to treat the dog and the environment on the same day.

Sprays or foggers (one per room) can be used in the house to kill fleas and ticks. The use of these insecticides must be preceded by a thorough vacuuming; special attention should be paid to the areas under furniture, near pet bedding, and along moldings. A product containing an IGR and an adulticide should be used as well. Foggers may not reach under furniture. A spray can be used in those areas where a fogger does not penetrate. Follow label instructions for the proper use of and precautions concerning sprays and foggers.

If a long-lasting spot-on adulticide is used, it may not be necessary to treat the environment as long as the client understands that fleas must have contact with the animal's hair before they are killed. However, if the pet is flea allergic, environmental treatment is essential, as just one flea bite can cause intense itching for several days.

Internal Parasites

Heartworms

Adult heartworms *(Dirofilaria immitis)* reside in the pulmonary arteries and in the right side of the heart. They produce larvae called microfilariae, which circulate in the blood for up to 2 years. These microfilariae are ingested by a feeding mosquito, molt to an infective stage in the mosquito's abdomen, and are injected into a new host when the mosquito feeds. They migrate through the body of the new host for several months before finally lodging in the heart and pulmonary vessels as mature adults. Microfilariae cannot mature into adult heartworms without first passing through a mosquito. In rare instances a bitch may pass microfilariae to her puppies through the placenta. These microfilariae will be in the blood but cannot cause an active infection.

Testing Procedures

Many dogs with heartworm infection have microfilariae in their blood; some have occult infections where heartworms are present but do not produce microfilariae. In-hospital antigen or antibody blood tests will detect the presence of adult heartworms in either case.

Thoracic radiography can also be used to diagnose heartworm disease. Long-standing heartworm infections produce visible, predictable pathology in the heart and lungs of infected dogs.

Prevention and Treatment

Heartworm infection can be prevented by administering oral medications to heartworm-negative dogs on a regular basis. Puppies should be started on heartworm prophylaxis as early as 6 weeks of age.

Heartworm preventive medication should be administered regularly in areas where the disease occurs. It may be suspended during the winter if mosquitoes are not present.

Heartworm-positive dogs should be treated as soon as possible to minimize liver, kidney, lung, and heart pathology and to minimize risk of transmission to other dogs.

Gastrointestinal Parasites

Gastrointestinal parasites can cause serious disorders in dogs, including life-threatening anemia, hypoproteinemia, diarrhea, vomiting, hypoglycemia, intestinal obstruction, and weight loss. Puppies are particularly susceptible. The most common parasites found in dogs are hookworms, roundworms (ascarids), whipworms, tapeworms, *Giardia* spp., and coccidia. The method of infection varies with the type of worm but includes transplacental transfer, transmission via the milk while nursing, skin penetration, and oral ingestion.

Certain canine parasites, such as hookworms, roundworms, at least three species of tapeworms, heartworms, and several intestinal protozoa including *Giardia* spp., can be transferred to humans. Therefore caution should be exercised when working with animals and their waste products.

Humans may become infected with canine roundworm *(Toxocara)* larvae. In humans larvae migrate extensively through the body and cause a variety of signs. The most common signs involve the gastrointestinal system or lungs. More devastating are blindness or neurologic signs. Because of the high frequency of prenatal *Toxocara* infections in pups, prophylactic treatment is recommended before eggs can be passed in the stool. Pups should be treated at 2, 5, and 11 weeks old. Two treatments, 2 weeks apart, are sufficient for newly acquired, weaned puppies. Lactating bitches should be treated at the same time as their offspring.

In addition to prophylactic roundworm treatment, puppies should be checked for internal parasites at 3 weeks, 6 to 8 weeks, 10 to 12 weeks, and 14 to 16 weeks of age; adults should be checked at least annually. The test requires a small sample of fresh feces, flotation solution (sodium nitrate solution with a specific gravity of 1.2 works best), and a compound microscope. The fecal sample is suspended in flotation solution, topped with a coverslip, and allowed to stand undisturbed for 5 to 10 minutes. A 24 hour flotation may be required for accurate evaluation of protozoal infection. The coverslip is then placed on a glass slide and examined for parasite ova. Whipworm ova will not float if the specific gravity of the flotation solution is not adequate. Tapeworm infections are rarely diagnosed by fecal examinations because the eggs are contained within segments of the tapeworm (proglottids), which crawl out of the dog's anus and fall to the ground. Commercially produced test kits can also be obtained to identify parasite ova in feces.

Treatment includes immediate therapy with appropriate anthelmintics (deworming medications), followup therapy 2 to 4 weeks later to kill migrating stages of the parasite, and cleanup of the environment to prevent reinfection.

BEHAVIOR PROBLEMS
Aggression*

The two most common manifestations of aggressive behavior toward humans are fear biting and dominance-related aggression. Fear biting is most commonly seen in a dog raised without appropriate human contact during the socialization period of growth (6 to 12 weeks of age). Such an animal fears people who are unfamiliar to it, and it may attempt to bite when feeling threatened. Treatment consists of desensitization and counterconditioning techniques to alleviate the dog's fear of humans. Drug therapy has been used in dogs, but its efficacy has not been established. Castration does not stop fear biting. Referral to a veterinary behaviorist for behavioral problems can be helpful if done at a young age.

More complete discussion of canine aggression can be found in Textbook of Veterinary Internal Medicine, *ed 4. Philadelphia, WB Saunders, 1995, and* Readings in Companion Animal Behavior. *Trenton, NJ, Veterinary Learning Systems, 1996.*

When a dog shows aggression toward members of the owner's family rather than strangers, the animal is probably attempting to establish dominance over those family members. This condition can be successfully treated with behavior modification, environmental manipulation, and, sometimes, drug therapy.

Other causes for canine aggression toward people include pain-induced aggression, hyperkinesis (overactivity), territorial aggression, and parental protectiveness.

Isolation from canine contacts between 4 to 7 weeks of age can also result in behavior problems manifested in adulthood as acts of aggression toward other dogs. This behavior should not be confused with intermale or territorial aggression.

Treatment for intermale and intraspecies aggression not related to territorial defense includes castration, counterconditioning programs, and drug therapy.

Coprophagy

Although the ingestion of feces is not harmful to the dog (other than the possibility of reacquisition of internal parasites), it is socially unacceptable to dog owners. The cause for this behavior is not known, but the possibilities include nutritional deficiencies (unlikely) and boredom (likely). This behavior can become an acquired habit. Coprophagy can be discouraged by promptly eliminating fecal matter from the environment and increasing the dog's exercise or play period. Commercial products are available to make the feces unpalatable.

Separation Anxiety

Separation anxiety is often seen in poorly socialized dogs. The behavior may be manifested as destruction of household items, excessive vocalization, digging, chewing, urination, and defecation. It is recommended that animals exhibiting such behavior not be crated or otherwise confined because they could injure themselves. Separation anxiety should be differentiated from the chewing and lapse in house-training a playful puppy may engage in.

Treatment of separation anxiety includes behavior modification and drug therapy. Referral to a veterinary behaviorist leads to a good prognosis for resolution of this problem. The addition of a companion animal to the household is controversial. Puppies should be confined to a small area with minimal access to furnishings and other belongings when left alone to prevent destructive behavior such as chewing, urination, and defecation.

Inappropriate Urination

Lapses in bladder control can be caused by disease conditions, anxiety, urine marking, or a lack of house-training. Once the cause is known, a treatment plan can be formulated to solve the problem. Disease conditions and anxiety can be cured with medical therapy. House-training problems can be solved by retraining the dog as if it were a puppy (i.e., confinement and the of a regular feeding and elimination schedule [see House-Training, p. 128]). Urine marking, mounting behavior, and roaming can be controlled by castration or drug therapy.

DIET AND FEEDING

Dogs eat to meet their energy needs. The quantity of food a dog requires each day depends on the caloric density of the product, the dog's physiologic status, age, activity level, and temperament, and the season of the year. The chosen product must have all required nutrients balanced to its caloric density. It is the calories, not the dry matter, that count.

A dog food should be chosen based on animal feeding studies to support the nutritional claim. Association of American Feed Control Officials (AAFCO) has recommended protocols that a manufacturer can follow to validate a nutritional claim. Look for a statement like "Animal feeding trials using AAFCO procedures show that [brand] provides 100% complete and balanced nutrition for [life stage]." This statement on a pet food package indicates that all criteria have been met for the particular life-stage nutritional claims.

Regulations require that products that are labeled as containing complete and balanced nutrition must have feeding directions. Manufacturers that do feeding studies base their feeding instructions on the caloric density of the food compared with the estimated energy requirements of the dog. The directions are only a starting place because every animal has different energy requirements and nutrient intake needs.

All the nutrients can be in the food and the food can be highly digestible, but that doesn't guarantee that the dog will eat it. The product selected not only needs to contain high-quality ingredients but it must be highly palatable as well.

Dogs should always have plenty of fresh, cool water available.

Recommendations for Weaning

Weaning is a stressful time for the lactating bitch and its offspring. Weaning begins when the puppies are first offered a gruel of a high-quality dry or canned puppy food at 3 to 4 weeks of age. The food should be offered up to four times each day for 10 to 15 minutes or until the puppies have eaten their fill. The puppies are then allowed to nurse until the next feeding period. Over a 2 week period, the puppies are allowed to eat more of the puppy food gruel and nurse for shorter periods. Final weaning should occur over a 5 to 7 day period. During this time the bitch should be given reduced amounts of food until it reaches its maintenance level of intake by the seventh day and the puppies should be allowed to nurse only once each day (to reduce the discomfort felt by the dam). Always provide plenty of fresh water.

Feeding Puppies

After starting puppies on a gruel of a high-quality puppy food when they are 3 weeks of age, the amount of water added to the food can be gradually reduced over a couple of weeks until it is fed as is.

Puppy diets **should not be supplemented.** If an AAFCO-tested diet was selected, it will contain all the nutrients needed in the right proportions to each other and balanced to the energy (caloric) density of the diet. Puppies should be fed all they can consume in a 15 to 20 minute period. Feed four times a day from weaning to 3 months of age, three times a day until 8 months of age, and then twice a day until maturity (about 9 to 12 months of age for small breeds, 12 to 18 months for large breeds, and as late as 24 months for giant breeds).

Feeding Adults

Adult dogs do not need high protein, high energy diets unless they are working dogs, bitches in the last trimester of pregnancy, or lactating dams. Small or medium sized adult dogs should be fed a good quality, complete and balanced maintenance diet once daily; large breeds

should be fed twice daily if possible. The amount fed should be sufficient to maintain a lean body condition. Healthy, mature dogs fed a
complete and balanced food do not normally require vitamin and mineral supplements.

Bitches that are pregnant or lactating will require up to three times
the maintenance energy (and nutrient) intake. These requirements can
be met through multiple feedings of a high quality product designed for
all life stages (remember to look for the AAFCO statement) or a high
quality puppy food. Using a puppy food for the bitch before whelping
helps simplify the weaning process later on.

Feeding Older Adults

Life stage feeding, which includes special products for older dogs,
helps the pet owner in the feeding process. Older pets are less active. A
senior diet is lower in calories, reducing the chances of obesity, is for-
tified with higher levels of water-soluble vitamins to replace those lost,
and contains lower amounts of higher quality protein so that the
nitrogenous wastes are reduced. With a high quality senior diet, exercise, and care, an older dog's quality of life can continue for a long
time.

Therapeutic Diets

Products intended as adjuncts to the treatment of disease are available only from veterinarians. If such a product is intended for long-term
feeding, look for the statement "Animal feeding trials using AAFCO
procedures show that (brand) provides 100% complete and balanced
nutrition for adult maintenance." Without this statement, the product is
suitable for short-term use only.

Bibliography

Bellows J: Veterinary dentistry. *Pedigree Breeder Forum* 6(1):3–13, 1997.
Concannon PW, Lein DH: Canine reproductive biology. *Kal Kan Forum*
    5(4):9–11, 1986.
Dillon R: Canine heartworm disease. *Pedigree Breeder Forum* 3(4):19–23,
    1994.
Georgi JR, Georgi ME: *Canine Clinical Parasitology.* Baltimore, Williams &
    Wilkins, 1992.
Gortel K: Advances in topical and systemic therapy for flea control in dogs.
    Canine Pract 22(2–3):16–21, 1997.

Harvey CE: *Veterinary Dentistry.* Philadelphia, WB Saunders, 1985.

Hawkins J: *Basic Canine Dentistry* (video/manual program). Vernon, CA, Waltham USA, Inc, 1997.

Holmstrom SE, Frost P, Gammon RL: *Veterinary Dental Techniques.* Philadelphia, WB Saunders, 1992.

Horwitz D: Aggressive behavior in dogs. *Pedigree Breeder Forum* 4(4):11–16, 1995.

Horwitz D: Puppy socialization—Getting off to a good start. *Pedigree Breeder Forum* 3(4):3–9, 1994.

Hoskins JD: Practices in modern vaccination. *Vet Tech* 13:51–55, 1992.

Hoskins JD: *Veterinary Pediatrics: Dogs and Cats From Birth to Six Months,* ed 2. Philadelphia, WB Saunders, 1995.

Houpt KA, Reisner IR: Behavioral disorders, in Ettinger SJ, Feldman EC (eds): *Textbook of Veterinary Internal Medicine,* ed 4. Philadelphia, WB Saunders, 1995.

Hribernik TN: Canine and feline heartworm disease, in Kirk RW, Bonagura JD (eds): *Current Veterinary Therapy X.* Philadelphia, WB Saunders, 1989, pp 263–270.

Johnson CA, Grace JA: Care of newborn puppies and kittens. *Kal Kan Forum* 6(1):9–16, 1987.

Kirk RW, Bonagura JD: *Current Veterinary Therapy XI.* Philadelphia, WB Saunders, 1992, pp 202–206.

Kirk RW, Bistner SI, Ford RB: *Handbook of Veterinary Procedures and Emergency Treatment,* ed 5. Philadelphia, WB Saunders, 1990, pp 758–773.

MacDonald JM: Current concepts on flea and tick control. *Pedigree Breeder Forum* 6(2):16–24, 1997.

Markwell P: *Waltham Applied Clinical Nutrition of the Dog and Cat.* Vernon, CA, Waltham USA, Inc, 1998.

Official Publication of Association of American Feed Control Officials, Inc. College Station, TX, AAFCO, 1993.

Smith C: Are we vaccinating too much? *JAVMA* 207(4):421, 1995.

Smith C: *Get Rid of Fleas and Ticks for Good!* Leavenworth, WA, Smith Veterinary Services, 1995.

Voith VL, Borchelt PL (eds): *Readings in Companion Animal Behavior.* Trenton, NJ, Veterinary Learning Systems, 1996.

Wills JM, Simpson KW: *The Waltham Book of Clinical Nutrition of the Dog and Cat.* Oxford, England, Pergamon Press, 1994.

Zimmer JF: Intestinal parasites of dogs and cats. *Kal Kan Forum* 5(4):12–18, 1986.

Zoonosis Updates. Schaumburg, IL, AVMA, 1990, pp 118–122.

FELINE CARE

FELINE DATA CHART

Life span	10–30 years
Normal body temperature	100.5°–102.5°F (38°–39.1°C)
Respiration	20–30 breaths per minute
Pulse	160–240 per minute
Blood collection sites	Cephalic vein, jugular vein, medial saphenous vein
Normal hemogram values	Hematocrit: 30%–45% White blood cells: 5,500–19,500/cu mm Total protein: 6.3–8.7 g/dl
Breeding information	
• **Puberty**	Queens: 4–18 months of age; tomcats: 8–10 months of age
• **Breeding season**	Seasonally polyestrus (spring through fall)
• **Gestation**	56–65 days (avg. 63); kittens are palpable from day 20–30 and 50–63, visible ultrasonographically after day 28, and visible radiographically after day 38
• **Litter size**	1–8 kittens (avg. 4)
• **Signs of estrus**	Vocalization, provocative behavior, attracts males, elevates tail, treads with hind feet
Neonates	Eyes and ears open at 10–16 days Kittens weaned at 6 weeks
Sexing	Mature male has externalized testes; in young kittens, the male anogenital orifices resemble a colon (:), whereas the female anogenital orifices resemble a semicolon (;)

BATHING

Cats do not usually require baths because they are fastidious groomers. Combing the hair coat daily reduces the amount of hair found on furniture and helps decrease the formation of hairballs, which may cause anorexia, vomiting, and gastrointestinal obstruction. Daily combing of long-haired cats removes small tangles, which may become large hair mats if left unattended. If there are any hair mats, it is not a good idea to use scissors to cut them off. Cats, like dogs, have loose skin and it is very easy to cut off a piece of skin or part of their ear. Mats can be removed more safely with clippers.

Protective Gear

A shaking cat can splash shampoos or dips into your unprotected eyes, and many pesticides may be absorbed through the skin. There are risks of both short-term and long-term exposure to pesticide dips and shampoos. Always wear a waterproof apron, gloves, and goggles to protect yourself.

Procedure

Apply sterile ophthalmic ointment to each eye to protect the cat's corneas from shampoo irritation. Place a cotton ball in each ear to prevent water from entering.

Allowing the cat to cling to an object, such as a towel or a window screen, can help the animal feel more secure and reduce the danger of scratches to the handler. Keep a tight grasp on the scruff of the cat's neck with one hand while bathing and rinsing with the other hand. Some cats are best bathed under sedation. Use a gentle shampoo to avoid stripping the hair coat of its natural protective oils. Diluting the shampoo with water before application will help promote lathering. Rinsing with demineralized water may reduce allergens contained in cat hair.

REPRODUCTION

Cats do not ovulate unless they are bred. If the queen is not bred, estrus recurs at 14 to 19 day intervals. While in heat the queen is receptive for 1 to 4 days. Should a sterile mating occur, the queen may experience pseudopregnancy for 40 days but rarely shows nesting behavior or mammary gland development.

Contraception

The best methods of contraception are ovariohysterectomy (spaying) in female cats and castration (neutering) in males (see Surgery, p. 151).

These surgical procedures are permanent and irreversible. There is no need for a queen to go through a first heat or to have a litter before being spayed.

Preparation for Queening

Queens become restless the last week of gestation. They should be introduced to the nest box at this time. The box should be covered and large enough for the cat to stretch out or stand up in. It should be located in a quiet, warm (minimum 70°F), dimly lit area that is isolated from other animals. The floor of the nest box should be covered with clean towels, blankets, or cloth.

Milk production begins 24 hours before queening. Impending parturition is signaled by vulvar enlargement and the presence of mucus at the vaginal orifice.

Cats in labor rarely need help. However, a queen that is having strong contractions and has not expelled a kitten within 2 hours probably needs veterinary attention. It is possible for kittens to be born several days apart if the queen was bred multiple times over a period of several days. A placenta should be expelled after each kitten. Complications are uncommon, although nervous queens have been known to savage (cannibalize) their young.

KITTEN CARE
Neonatal Development

Kittens are helpless at birth. They rely on the queen for food, warmth, and elimination of body wastes. The queen stimulates urination and defecation after each feeding by licking the kittens' anogenital area.

By 6 days of age the kittens can regulate their own body temperature. Their eyes open between days 10 and 16, and the ears open a day or so later. By 2 to 3 weeks of age they can walk and groom themselves.

Nursing and Weaning

The queen spends 70% of its time nursing the kittens. It will not leave the kittens for 24 to 48 hours after parturition, so food, water, and a litter pan should be placed close by.

During the first 24 to 36 hours, the kittens receive colostrum from the queen, which contains maternal antibodies to protect them from infectious diseases. They nurse every 1 to 2 hours for the first week.

At 4 weeks of age a complete and balanced canned cat food or a mushy gruel of commercial kitten food blended with water should be offered several times a day (see Diet and Feeding, p. 157). The queen will return to estrus during the fourth to sixth week of lactation and is fertile at this time. In an ideal situation, the kittens should be weaned between 8 and 12 weeks of age.

Housing

A small box with high sides placed in a warm, draft-free location is an ideal environment. The floor should be padded with washable towels or disposable diapers.

Because a kitten is unable to regulate its body temperature for the first 5 days of life, orphan kittens require an external source of heat. A wrapped heating pad should be placed on a low setting to create an ambient temperature of 86°F for the first week postpartum, 80°F the second and third weeks, and 75°F thereafter. A small area on the floor of the box should be left unheated so the kitten can move away from the heat source if it gets too warm.

Nutrition

A kitten should gain 10 to 15 g of body weight per day for the first 5 months of life. If necessary, the animal can be fed by a syringe or baby nurser (the formula should slowly ooze through a premature infant nipple) or by tube feeding.

Orphan Kittens

The best way to raise an orphan kitten is to foster it onto a lactating

AMOUNT OF FORMULA TO FEED PER DAY	
Week of Life	*Amount per 100 g body weight*
1	13 ml
2	17 ml
3	20 ml
4	22 ml

queen. Queens will often adopt kittens that are up to 2 weeks older or younger than their own offspring. The queen will provide warmth, food, and constant attention. If a foster dam is not available, the kitten must be hand raised.

Orphan Kitten Formula

Use a commercially prepared queen's milk substitute. Follow the manufacturer's instructions for preparation. Orphans should be fed at least four times a day.

After each meal, the kitten's anogenital areas should be swabbed with moist cotton to stimulate urination and defecation. Formula feeding should continue until the kitten is eating solid food. At 4 weeks of age, a nutritionally complete and balanced canned food or a mushy gruel made from dry food can be offered several times a day.

LITTER TRAINING

Cats are clean, fastidious creatures. By instinct they will not soil their beds and prefer to hide their body wastes from view once they have eliminated. This behavior facilitates litter box training.

There are many types of litter that can be used, including clay litter, clumping litter, sand, and dirt. Cats usually show a preference for certain types of litter, and some cats prefer a covered litter box to an open one.

The training begins by confining the kitten to a very small area that contains food, water, toys, a sleeping area, and the litter box. Successful elimination in the litter box should be lavishly praised. If the cat urinates or defecates on the floor, the feces or urine-soaked paper towel should be put in the litter box and lightly covered with litter and the floor should be cleaned thoroughly with an odor-masking disinfectant. The confined area should be made smaller if more accidents occur and can be expanded gradually as the kitten consistently uses the box.

Some cats will refuse to use a dirty litter box, so feces and urine-soaked litter must be removed from the box daily. The litter should be changed completely and the box should be disinfected twice a week to control odors. Household baking soda can be added to the litter to control odors. Cats do not like to share litter boxes. A separate box should be provided for each animal, and each box should remain in the same place at all times. If the box is moved to a new location, the cat may eliminate on the floor of the original site of the box.

DENTAL CARE*

A tooth consists of a core of dentin covered with enamel at the crown and cementum at the root. At the center of a tooth is a bundle of epithelial tissues made up of nerves and blood vessels (the dental pulp).

Cats have four types of teeth: incisors, canines, premolars, and molars. Each tooth performs a different function (tearing, shearing, grinding) in mastication.

Cats are diphyodont animals; they produce a deciduous generation of teeth that are shed and replaced by permanent teeth when the jaw bones attain their mature size. The deciduous incisors are the first teeth to emerge through the gums and are usually present in kittens by 2 to 3 weeks of age. Full deciduous dentition is present by 7 to 8 weeks of age, and a cat will have a complete set of permanent teeth by the time it is 6 months old.

The maxillary (upper) incisors of a normal cat should slightly overlap the mandibular (lower) incisors. A large space is present between the cat's canine and premolar teeth. Short-faced breeds, such as Persians, may have an undershot incisor relationship (i.e., the maxilla is considerably shorter than the mandible).

Retained deciduous teeth and extra permanent (supernumerary) teeth are problems occasionally seen in cats. Both conditions cause crowding of permanent teeth with resultant malocclusion. Retained or extra teeth should be removed promptly.

Dental hygiene is important in cats. Plaque and dental calculus accumulate on teeth at the gumline and cause irritation that can predispose the animal to dental caries (often referred to as cervical line lesions or odontoclastic resorptive lesions) and periodontal disease. Gingivitis (inflammation of the gum tissues) may also occur secondary to plaque accumulation, although a chronic, unresponsive condition may indicate a more serious underlying disease such as that caused by feline leukemia virus, feline immunodeficiency virus, or calicivirus.

More details about feline dental care are provided in Waltham Feline Dentistry, *a video/manual package for veterinary hospital staff that can be purchased by calling 1-888-371-7900.*

DETERMINING A KITTEN'S AGE BY DENTITION

Teeth	Age at Which Teeth Appear
Deciduous[a]	
Incisors	14–21 days
Canines	21–28 days
Upper third premolars	28–35 days
Upper first premolar	35–60 days
Full dentition	7–8 weeks
Permanent[b]	
Incisors	3½–4 months
Premolars	5–6 months
Molars	4–5 months
Canines	5–6 months
Full dentition	6 months

[a]Full deciduous dentition:
    Maxillary teeth—6 incisors, 2 canines, 6 premolars
    Mandibular teeth—6 incisors, 2 canines, 4 premolars
[b]Full permanent dentition
    Maxillary teeth—6 incisors, 2 canines, 6 premolars, 2 molars
    Mandibular teeth—6 incisors, 2 canines, 4 premolars, 2 molars

Cats should have their teeth professionally cleaned at least once a year. The procedure requires an overnight fast and general anesthesia (see p. 130 in the Canine Care section). Cleaning the teeth at home weekly with a cat toothbrush (or a gauze pad) and meat-based toothpaste is recommended. Do not use baking soda or human toothpaste in the cat. Dry food may help reduce plaque accumulation.

SURGERY
Spaying (Ovariohysterectomy)

Spaying is an irreversible means by which a female cat is rendered sterile. The procedure involves complete removal of the uterus and ovaries. Spayed cats will not come into heat.

A cat reaches puberty between 5 and 18 months of age and can be spayed as early as 6 weeks of age. The operation is preceded by an overnight fast and requires general anesthesia as well as a full day's hospitalization. Complications are rare but may include postsurgical hemorrhage, tissue reaction to ligature material, uterine stump pyometra, and infection of the incision.

Postoperative care includes restricting exercise (no jumping or climbing) for a week and checking the incision daily for signs of inflammation. The sutures are removed 7 to 10 days after the surgery.

Castration (Orchiectomy)

Male cats can be castrated as early as 6 weeks of age. The procedure renders the tomcat permanently sterile. Both testes are removed while the cat is under general anesthesia. In younger cats the scrotal incision is not sutured and heals within 24 to 48 hours, but suturing is recommended in older cats. The animal may be released from the hospital on the day of surgery or observed overnight. Complications are unusual but may include postsurgical hemorrhage and infection of the incision.

Postoperatively, shredded paper should be used in place of cat litter for a few days to avoid the introduction of litter into the incision and the scrotal area should be checked daily for signs of inflammation. The cat should not be allowed to roam freely for a week.

Behavioral changes seen after castration include decreased incidences of urine spraying, fighting, and roaming. Cats that are castrated before reaching puberty (about 6 months of age) do not develop the physical characteristics (big head, thick neck, odoriferous urine) associated with intact tomcats.

Declawing
Onychectomy

Cats can be declawed as early as 6 to 12 weeks of age. The procedure entails complete removal of the third phalanx and claw of each toe. Although the surgery can be done on all four paws, it is recommended that only the front feet be declawed so the cat can use its hind claws for protection.

The procedure is performed under general anesthesia. Tissue adhesives or absorbable sutures are used to close the wounds, and the feet are bandaged to control bleeding. Complications include hemorrhage, infection of the wounds, and regrowth of the nails. The bandages are removed 24 hours after the surgery; if the bleeding has stopped, the cat can be released from the hospital.

Postoperatively, the cat should be kept indoors for 1 week and shredded paper should be used in place of litter to reduce the possibility of wound contamination. Removal of sutures is usually not necessary. The cat's paws will be sore for 2 to 3 weeks.

Deep Digital Flexor Tendonectomy

A less traumatic approach to declawing involves transection of the deep digital flexor tendons, which prevents the cat from using its claws for scratching. This procedure requires general anesthesia. The skin incision must be sutured following the tendonectomy, but bandaging is not necessary. The animal should be able to walk comfortably within 24 hours. Postoperatively, it is important to trim the nails every 4 to 8 months.

VACCINATIONS

Cats should be vaccinated on a regular basis against life-threatening infectious diseases, including upper respiratory diseases (viral rhinotracheitis and feline calicivirus), and feline panleukopenia (distemper). Vaccination for feline leukemia virus should be considered if the cat is at risk of exposure. A feline pneumonitis vaccine may also be given to kittens living in catteries or multicat households where *Chlamydia*-induced upper respiratory infections are a problem.

A queen transmits protective immunity to the kittens via colostrum during the first 24 to 36 hours after parturition. Colostrum contains maternal antibodies that protect the kittens until their own immune systems are functional. The length of maternal protection varies from animal to animal and can last from 3 to 15 weeks.

Rabies vaccination requirements vary from state to state and will vary within states depending on local ordinances. Although rabies vaccination is required for dogs throughout the United States, there are no laws in place requiring vaccination of cats in many states. As a result, the prevalence of rabies in cats is greater than that in dogs; in 1995, for example, there were 146 documented cases of rabies in dogs vs. 288 cases in cats.

Once the vaccination series is completed, boosters should be given according to the vaccine manufacturer's recommendation.

There is concern that any modified-live virus vaccine can induce neoplasia in cats. Although the prevalence of postvaccinal sarcomas is unknown, it may be as high as 1 in 1000 vaccinated cats. Vaccine-

FELINE VACCINATION PROTOCOLS

Vaccine	Initial Administration (Weeks of Age)	Booster	Recommendations
Panleukopenia virus	9 and 12 Repeat 12 months later	Every 3 years	Recommended for all cats
Herpesvirus-1/ Calicivirus (injectable)	9 and 12 Repeat 12 months later	Every 1–3 years depending on risk	Recommended for all cats
Herpesvirus/ Calicivirus (intranasal)	9 and 12 Repeat 12 months later	Every 1–3 years depending on risk	Optional; may cause postvaccinal sneezing and oral lesions
Feline leukemia virus	9 and 12	Annual	Recommended for cats at risk
Chlamydia psittaci	9 and 12	Annual	Optional; use should be limited to those households where infection is confirmed or highly suspected
FIP virus	16 and 20	Annual	Optional; of uncertain value
Rabies virus	12 or 16 Actual age may be established by local statutes	Every 1 to 3 years as required by state or local law	Required; does not meet legal requirements if administered by unauthorized person

See the 1998 Report of the American Association of Feline Practitioners and Academy of Feline Medicine Advisory Panel on Feline Vaccines, *JAVMA* 212(2):227, 1998.

induced sarcomas are extremely aggressive and are associated with a grave long-term prognosis. The only available approach is to attempt to control the tumor through complete surgical excision; radiation therapy is believed to aid in control. However, most tumors recur and eventually kill the cat.

PARASITES

Fleas and Ticks

To successfully control fleas and ticks, these pests must be eliminated from both the animal and the environment. Much of the information on fleas and ticks found in the Canine Care section (pp. 136–137) is applicable to cats as well.

However, cats are more sensitive to chemicals than are dogs. Use extreme care when treating cats or even when treating dogs that live in the same household as a cat. In general, insect growth regulators and short-acting pyrethrins are safe for use on cats as are the newer spot-on/spray adulticides that are approved for cats.

Internal Parasites

Gastrointestinal parasites are common in cats. The clinical signs of infection vary with the type and number of worms present and can be particularly severe in kittens. Anemia, vomiting, diarrhea, cough, difficulty breathing, unthriftiness, dull hair coat, a pot-bellied appearance, and the presence of grain-like organisms around the anus may be indicative of internal parasites. The most common parasites found in cats are tapeworms (carried by fleas or rodents), roundworms, hookworms, lungworms, and coccidia. The method of infection varies with the type of worm but includes transfer through the queen's milk, skin penetration, and oral ingestion.

Because humans may become infected with feline roundworm *(Toxascaris)* larvae, prophylactic treatment of kittens is recommended before any eggs are passed in the stool. Kittens should be treated at 2, 5, and 11 weeks of age. Two treatments, 2 weeks apart, are sufficient for newly acquired, weaned kittens. Lactating queens should be treated at the same time as their offspring. Human infection is very similar to *Toxocara* infection (see p. 138).

Kittens should be checked for worms at 9 and 12 weeks of age, and adults should be checked annually. A fecal flotation test (see p. 139) should be performed. Owners should be advised to watch for grain-sized tapeworm segments on the cat or in the litter box, as tapeworms are very difficult to detect on fecal tests. A sample of fresh feces should be taken to the hospital for analysis when parasitism is suspected.

The treatment for parasitism includes immediate therapy with appropriate anthelmintics (deworming medications) and follow-up therapy 2 to 4 weeks later to kill the migrating stages of the parasite.

Heartworms, which are carried by mosquitoes, can also infect cats. These parasites are difficult to detect in cats because cats are often infected with one worm only and are rarely microfilaremic. The presence of a single heartworm can be fatal to a cat, and there is no safe treatment for cats that are infected. Clinical signs include intermittent vomiting and a chronic cough. A heartworm preventive, like that given to dogs, can be administered to cats.

Certain feline parasites *(Toxoplasma gondii, Giardia* spp., hookworms, roundworms, and the tapeworm *Dipylidium caninum,* which is carried by fleas) are zoonotic organisms of public health significance. Therefore, caution should be exercised when working with animals and their waste products.

BEHAVIOR PROBLEMS
Aggression

The period of socialization for kittens begins around 4 weeks after birth and lasts 1 month. Animals that are deprived of social interaction with humans or other kittens during this period may not be able to later develop normal social relationships and may demonstrate behavioral problems upon reaching adulthood. These problems include rejection of or aggression toward humans (especially children), aggression toward other cats, failure to mate successfully, and rejection or cannibalism of offspring after queening. Counterconditioning techniques can be used to correct many of these problems.

Aggression between cats can be treated by castration of intact males and behavior modification and drug therapy for neutered males and females.

Elimination Problems

Cats that begin eliminating outside the litter box on a regular basis after being trained may do so for many reasons including illness, anxiety, an aversion to the type or location of the box or litter, or a preference for another location or litter. Cats do not like dirty litter, and some may not like to share litter boxes with other cats.

Once the cause of the problem is identified, measures to correct the abnormal behavior can be taken, such as environmental manipulation or drug therapy. Intact males that show urine marking ("spraying") behavior may require neutering. Although neutering may not stop spraying altogether, it substantially reduces its frequency in most cats.

Predatory Behavior

Cats are true carnivores and learn early in life how to hunt and catch prey. Hunting is a normal, instinctive behavior in cats. The only way an owner can discourage this type of behavior is to confine the animal indoors. Bells attached to the collar of a free-roaming cat may help alert potential prey to the presence of the cat.

DIET AND FEEDING

Normal, healthy cats are slow, discriminating eaters with a keen sense of taste. They may become addicted to particular shapes of dry foods. Cats require unusually high levels of protein in their diets as well as taurine (an essential aminosulfonic acid), preformed arachidonic acid, extra niacin, and preformed vitamin A. Cats need a high quality, well-balanced commercial cat food in amounts sufficient to maintain optimum body weight and condition. Dog food does not meet feline nutritional requirements and should not be fed to cats. Because of concerns about feline lower urinary tract disease, most commercial cat foods now contain controlled levels of magnesium and ingredients that result in urinary acidification. Cats with urinary problems require a complete diagnostic workup before dietary changes are recommended.

Unless obesity is a problem, cats should have unrestricted access to dry food or, if canned food is fed, a 6½ oz can should be divided into two feedings daily. This is sufficient for the average 7 to 8 lb cat. Very small amounts of a variety of low fat, low salt, cooked table scraps are acceptable for cats that are not overweight. Cats should not be fed bones, and they do not need dietary supplements if they are given adequate amounts of a high quality commercial cat food.

As with dog food, it is best to choose a product that has an AAFCO feeding statement. This ensures that the product has been tested and that it has passed the criteria necessary to support the nutritional claim.

Cats that become anorexic need special attention as it takes only a short period of time for some of these animals to develop hepatic lipidosis, a life-threatening liver disorder. Obese cats on too rapid a weight loss program may also develop hepatic lipidosis.

Gestation and Lactation

Pregnant cats gain weight gradually throughout the period of gestation, unlike dogs, in which most of the weight gain occurs in the last trimester. The amount of food offered to a pregnant cat should be gradually increased through gestation until queening, at which point the cat should be consuming a quantity that is 25% greater than its normal maintenance amount daily. A free choice feeding program works very well in pregnant cats as well as in lactating queens. Lactating cats require two to three times their normal maintenance requirement to maintain body weight and milk production.

Weaning and Kitten Diets

Kittens are entirely dependent on the milk of the queen for about 4 weeks, by which time they have usually tripled their birth weight and are beginning to explore their surroundings.

At 4 to 5 weeks the process of weaning or gradual replacement of the queen's milk with other food can begin. Weaning is a time of learning and is best done gradually to avoid upsets to the digestive system. The kitten must become accustomed to new tastes and textures of foods, and its digestive system must adapt to new kinds of proteins, fats, and carbohydrates. It is often suggested that the first new food should be milk based. Although most kittens will drink such foods, their use is not essential because most queens will continue to suckle until 7 or 8 weeks after parturition.

By the fifth week kittens are usually beginning to eat the queen's food and may eat finely minced or chopped moist food that is provided in a shallow dish for easy access. Because they eat only small amounts at first, it is best to use highly palatable, moist, meaty canned foods. Dry and semimoist foods are less palatable, and young kittens often refuse to eat enough of these products to support proper growth. Digestibility of dry foods is usually lower than that of canned cat food. Therefore dry foods are not as suitable for weanling kittens. By the time the kittens are 7 to 8 weeks old the proportion of their total nutrient intake coming from supplementary food should be at least 70% to

80%. Kittens can then be separated from their mother and be fed independently.

Geriatric Diets

Old cats may require highly palatable, highly digestible rations that contain increased levels of unsaturated fatty acids, zinc, and vitamins. Warming the food can increase its appeal by enhancing the smell and flavor. Cats should not be allowed to overeat, as obesity predisposes cats to many health problems.

Therapeutic Diets

Products for dietary management of disease are available only from veterinarians in canned meat and dry varieties. The key features to look for in these products are proof of clinical trials (given on the label), high quality ingredients, and pet enjoyment to ensure client compliance. The AAFCO nutrition statement can serve as your guide to a nutritionally complete product.

Bibliography

Chablis BL: Feline aggression. Classification, diagnosis and treatment. *Vet Clin North Am Small Anim Pract* 21:315–327, 1991.

Dillon R: Feline heartworms: More than just a curiosity. *Vet Forum,* p 18, Dec 1995.

Feldman EC, Nelson RW: Feline reproduction, in *Canine and Feline Endocrinology and Reproduction.* Philadelphia, WB Saunders, 1987, pp 525–548.

Hawkins J: *Feline Dentistry* (video/manual program). Vernon, CA, Waltham USA, Inc, 1997.

Hoskins JD: Practices in modern vaccination. *Vet Tech* 13:51–55, 1992.

Hoskins JD: Clinical evaluation of the kitten. *Vet Tech* 12:121–131, 1991.

Hoskins JD: *Veterinary Pediatrics: Dogs and Cats From Birth to Six Months,* ed 2. Philadelphia, WB Saunders, 1995.

Kirk RW, Bistner SI, Ford RB: *Handbook of Veterinary Procedures and Emergency Treatment,* ed 5. Philadelphia, WB Saunders, 1990, pp 910–916.

Krebs JW, Strine TW, Smith JS, et al: Rabies surveillance in the United States during 1995. *JAVMA* 109(12):1031–2044, 1996.

MacDonald JM: Current concepts on flea and tick control. *Pedigree Breeder Forum* 6(2):16–24, 1997.

Markwell P: *Waltham Applied Clinical Nutrition of the Dog and Cat.* Vernon, CA, Waltham USA, Inc, 1998.

McLear RC: Rabies: An update. *Pedigree Breeder Forum* 6(2):2–8, 1997.

Official Publication of Association of American Feed Control Officials, Inc. College Station, Texas, AAFCO, 1993.

Rife JN: Deep digital flexor tendonectomy—An alternative to amputation onychectomy for declawing cats. *JAAHA* 24:73–76, 1988.

Slatter DH: *Textbook of Small Animal Surgery,* ed 2. Philadelphia, WB Saunders Co, 1993.

Smith C: Changes and challenges in feline nutrition. *JAVMA* 203(10):1395–1400, 1993.

Voith VL, Borchelt PL (eds): *Readings in Companion Animal Behavior.* Trenton, NJ, Veterinary Learning Systems, 1996.

Wills JM, Simpson KW: *The Waltham Book of Clinical Nutrition of the Dog and Cat.* Oxford, England, Pergamon Press, 1994.

Wills JM: Energy requirements of dogs and cats. *Waltham Int Focus* 1(4):2–5, 1991.

Zimmer JF: Intestinal parasites of dogs and cats. *Kal Kan Forum* 5(4):12–18, 1986.

Zoonosis Updates. Schaumburg, IL, AVMA, 1990, pp 118–122.

EQUINE CARE

EQUINE DATA CHART

Life span	20–30 years
Breeds	
Horse breeds	Thoroughbred, Arabian, Morgan, Tennessee Walker, Standardbred, Saddlebred, Hanovarian, Paint, Mustang, Appaloosa, Paso Fino, Miniature Horse, many more
Draft breeds	Percheron, Belgian, Clydesdale, Shire
Pony breeds	Welsh, Connemara, Shetland
Normal body temperature	100.5°–102°F (38°–38.8°C)
Respiration	8–10 breaths per minute
Pulse	30–40 beats per minute
Blood collection sites	Jugular vein
Normal hemogram values	PCV: 32%–48% White blood cells: $6–12 \times 10^3/\mu l$ Total protein: 6–8.5 g/dl
Breeding information	
• **Puberty**	15–24 months
• **Breeding season**	April through September; artificial lights and hormonal therapy create earlier onset of cycling
• **Estrous cycle**	21 days
• **Estrus**	4–7 days, ovulation 24–48 hr before the end of estrus; breed once or twice daily beginning 2 days after onset of estrus or as indicated by rectal palpation of the ovaries
• **Signs of estrus**	Frequent urination and tail flagging for stallion, female stands to be mounted
• **Gestation**	340 days
• **Number of foals**	1

Neonates   Ensure adequate passive transfer
(maximum 1 to 2 liters of colostrum in
first 12 hours of life); wean at 4 to 6
months
Foals are born with all senses developed,
in contrast to puppies and kittens

HOUSING

The ideal housing for a horse is a run-in shed with access to a large area for exercise. The shed should have a roof and three sides to protect the horse from the elements. Horses that are kept in stalls or small paddocks must receive daily exercise.

Barns must be well ventilated and should not be artificially heated. An enclosed barn provides a breeding ground for bacteria and allows buildup of ammonia fumes and dust that can harm the horses' lungs.

It is not necessary for healthy adult horses to be kept inside, even in cold weather, if they have access to a run-in shed and are accustomed to the climate. Horses grow a thick hair coat that has a natural fluff. Covering that coat with a blanket flattens out its natural insulating ability. What's more, the digestion of hay provides horses with a significant source of internal heat.

On the other hand, horses kept in a barn much of the time, especially one that is heated, will not grow a thick coat and must be protected with a blanket during cold weather. Horses that are clipped to prevent excessive sweating, and older horses, which don't regulate body heat as well, may also need blanketing. Young foals must be sheltered on cold days but still need regular exercise.

DENTAL CARE

A horse's teeth grow continuously throughout its lifetime. As the teeth grow and the animal chews, the wearing surface of the teeth becomes flattened and sharp points may develop on the edges. This may cause the horse to drop its food while chewing, cut its cheeks while eating, or simply lose weight. The points can be removed with dental "floats" by the veterinarian or dental technician. Yearly dental examinations prevent problems from becoming severe. More frequent examinations are necessary for young horses (during tooth eruption) and older horses.

AGING A HORSE BY ITS TEETH: CHANGES IN THE LOWER INCISORS			
Stage	1st Incisor (Middle)	2nd Incisor	3rd Incisor (Outer)
Deciduous (baby)	6 days	6 weeks	6 months
Adult eruption	2½ years	3½ years	4½ years
Adult in wear	3 years	4 years	5 years
Loss of cup*	6 years	7 years	8 years
Star appears†	8 years	9 years	10 years

*The cup is an indentation in the surface of the tooth.
†The star is a blackish line that becomes rounded over the years, on the surface of the tooth.

VACCINATIONS

A wide variety of equine vaccines are available. Their use and frequency vary with the area of the country, the age of the horse, and its function. Veterinarians usually create custom vaccination schedules for their horse-owning clients. This schedule will list the vaccines recommended and the dates vaccine boosters are due. The length of time that each vaccine lasts differs with the vaccine. It is important to remember that the vaccines for influenza and rhinopneumonitis last only 3 to 4 months, so frequent boosters are necessary for complete protection.

PARASITES
External Parasites

Equine external parasites include the following:

♦ **Lice** are species-specific and are transmitted from horse to horse via grooming tools. They become a problem during winter and spring when the horse's coat is long. Signs of a louse problem include itching and hair loss along the mane, neck, and tail. Louse infestations are treated by administering oral medication or using a topical powder on the horse and by cleaning or applying louse dust to all grooming equipment and blankets.

♦ **Flies** are controlled with insecticidal spray or with fly parasites (small nonstinging wasps that eat fly larvae). Horse's eyes and ears may be protected by using a fly mask, a mesh hood that cov-

VACCINES AVAILABLE FOR HORSES

- ◆ Eastern, Western, and Venezuelan encephalitis
- ◆ Tetanus
- ◆ Influenza
- ◆ Rhinopneumonitis
- ◆ Rabies
- ◆ Potomac Horse fever
- ◆ Strangles
- ◆ Botulism *(Clostridium)*

ers the horse's head but still allows it to see out. A variety of flies infest horses:

—Stable flies, horn flies, horse flies, black flies, and deer flies bite the horse.

—Face flies feed on mucus draining from the horse's eyes, nose, and mouth.

—Blow flies lay eggs in wounds.

◆ **Gnats** *(Culicoides)* are tiny bloodsucking pests that cause itching of the mane, tail, or belly. Some horses develop allergies to their bites. Since gnats come out at night, horses can be protected by keeping them stabled from before dusk to after sunrise.

Internal Parasites

Equine internal parasites include the following:

◆ **Bloodworms** consist of large and small strongyles. The adult forms of both live in the large intestine.

—Larvae of large strongyles migrate through the liver, abdomen, and arteries before emerging as adults in the intestine. They can cause major damage to arterial walls.

—Small strongyle larvae penetrate the intestinal wall, where they form cysts that are resistant to many dewormers. The cysts tend to emerge en masse in the spring, sometimes causing colic.

◆ **Bots** are the larval stage of a fly. The bot fly lays eggs, which can be seen as small yellowish dots attached firmly to the hair, on the horse's legs. When the horse rubs its legs with its lips, the eggs hatch, releasing larvae that enter the horse's mouth and migrate to its stomach. Bot larvae attach to the stomach wall, where they live for up to a year. They are eventually passed in the manure, where they mature into flies.

♦ **Roundworms** parasitize the young horse. By the age of 2, horses have developed an immunity to this type of parasite. Roundworm larvae migrate through the liver and lungs, causing damage to both organs. Adults in the small intestine can lay millions of nearly indestructible eggs that pass in the manure. Young foals may be heavily infected starting from the day of their birth, but their fecal egg counts will be negative until adult worms begin to lay eggs.

♦ **Pinworms** are a nuisance parasite that live in the large intestine and cause anal itching.

♦ **Tapeworms** live in the cecum. Buildup of a large number of tapeworms may cause colic.

♦ **Threadworms** pass from mare's milk to young foals and are a common cause of foal diarrhea.

Deworming

A wide variety of dewormers are available for horses. As with the vaccine schedule, an individualized deworming schedule should be created for each horse, depending on its age and circumstances.

A few basic approaches to deworming are used. Some horses are dewormed every 2 months. Others are dewormed on a strategic schedule that takes weather and the seasons into account, with treatment given at times that horses are most likely to be infected or to pass worm eggs. A third option is to use a daily deworming medication in the feed.

There is also variation in the approach to rotating dewormers. Some veterinarians prefer to change the class of dewormer used each time the horse is treated. Others use the same product for up to a year and then switch to a different class of dewormer for the next period.

TRIMMING AND SHOEING

Horse hooves require trimming on a regular schedule. The interval varies among horses, but the average is 6 weeks.

The use of shoes is optional. Horses with feet that crack easily or that are ridden on rocks or hard ground need shoes to protect their feet.

Those that are not ridden or that are ridden only on soft ground may not.

Horses that have well-formed feet and no signs of lameness function well with premade shoes. Special shoes are made for a variety of disorders of the feet and legs.

LAMENESS

Lameness is a major cause of veterinary calls from horse owners. A thorough lameness examination is necessary to arrive at an accurate diagnosis. The horse must be observed walking, trotting, and performing a variety of tests. During the flexion test the horse's leg is held and a specific joint is flexed for a brief period. The horse is then asked to trot out, to see whether that flexion worsened the lameness. Injection of a local anesthetic is sometimes used to pinpoint the exact location of an injury. When the sore area is anesthetized, the formerly lame horse trots off soundly.

Once the location of the injury is found, further diagnostic tests are required to pinpoint its cause. These tests may include ultrasound or radiography.

COLIC

Colic is used to describe any disorder that causes pain in the abdomen; it is not a specific diagnosis. It represents another major cause of veterinary calls from horse owners.

Colic may be caused by intestinal parasites, impaction, gas, intestinal twisting, or bad feed. Signs include kicking at the belly, rolling, sweating, pawing, and lack of appetite. Some horses stop passing manure. The degree of pain a horse is showing is not always related to the severity of the problem.

Colic is an emergency that requires prompt treatment. Some cases respond to medical treatment, whereas others require surgery.

BEHAVIOR PROBLEMS
Stall Vices

Stall vices include wood chewing, stall walking, and kicking the stall walls. These vices may be due to lack of adequate forage or result from boredom. Horses that do not have access to pasture may fulfill their need to graze by chewing on wood. "Windsucking" differs from wood chewing in that the horse does not chew, but grasps the surface with its teeth and sucks in air. This vice is thought to start because of boredom and continues as a bad habit that can be very hard to break.

Many of these vices can be reduced or prevented by allowing access to pasture or providing other equine company (or a goat) or toys such as a large rubber ball. Other solutions include allowing more exercise and feeding a higher percentage of hay in the total ration.

Spray products with a bad taste may be applied to wood fencing to discourage chewing. Products that are irritating to the mucous membranes should be avoided. Windsucking can be limited by applying a muzzle or by the use of neck straps that restrict the horse's ability to perform that movement.

Riding Problems

A wide variety of behavior problems occur when horses are being ridden. Most of these should be brought to an expert trainer's attention, as should problems that arise when trailering a horse. Occasionally, a health problem causes the behavior; for example, a sore back may cause a horse to resist being saddled or mounted, or a sore mouth may cause problems with the bit. Any horse with a behavior problem that does not resolve with training should receive a thorough physical examination.

Restraint

A halter and lead rope are used for basic restraint of the horse. When moderate distraction is needed, one can grasp a fold of skin along the horse's neck. A nose twitch, properly applied, should distract the horse and not cause any harm. Lip or nose chains should be used with care, such that pressure is the result of the horse's behavior only.

DIET AND FEEDING

Horses are grazing animals that require water and forage. Either hay or pasture may be provided. Nutritional needs of adult horses with a mild to moderate exercise schedule are easily met with a good quality grass or grass-alfalfa hay mix or equivalent pasture. Horses on hay alone will eat from 1% to 3% of their body weight per day in hay (20 lb of hay for a 1000 lb horse), divided into at least two feedings. Hay should be fed by weight, not by "flakes," since the size of a flake varies.

Hay or pasture may be supplemented to add calories or to add vitamins or minerals. Horses eating low quality pasture (brown, end-of-season) or hay (dusty, old, or brownish) may need either or both of these.

Extremely athletic horses may not be able to consume a large enough quantity of hay to meet their energy needs. These horses may receive grain or even vegetable oil to supplement their diets. Grain should be weighed, since a "1 lb coffee can" full of corn weighs more than the same can full of oats. The weight of grain should never exceed the weight of hay fed, with the total amount of feed (hay plus grain) not exceeding 2% to 3% of the horse's body weight per day.

The growing horse and pregnant or nursing mare have additional needs for calories, protein, and a specific calcium:phosphorus balance. A high quality alfalfa or grass-alfalfa mix will usually meet their nutritional needs. Calcium or phosphorus supplements are added if necessary according to the type of hay and/or grain provided. A veterinarian should help balance the ration and determine the supplements needed. Nutritional analysis of the feed may be needed.

A trace mineral salt block should be provided to horses. Horses that sweat profusely during exercise may need electrolyte supplements during exercise.

All horses require a continuous supply of fresh water. There are a wide variety of water heaters available to prevent water from freezing during winter. Horses cannot get sufficient water from eating snow.

Older horses may have problems with their teeth and may not digest food efficiently. Providing pelleted feed or a feed made for older horses can help (a veterinarian can give specific recommendations).

Obesity is common in horses and is usually due to overfeeding or to feeding higher calorie hay than is necessary. Overweight horses may be fed a diet of grass hay alone. Those on pasture should be limited in their grazing time.

Bibliography

Lewis LD: *Equine Clinical Nutrition.* Philadelphia, Williams & Wilkins, 1995.
Smith C: *Easy Health Care For Your Horse.* New York, Prentice Hall, 1991.

FOOD ANIMAL CARE

CATTLE
DATA CHART

Life span

Dairy cattle: 12–16 years (herd life = 6 years avg.)
Beef cattle: 12–16 years

Breeds

Dairy: The most common breeds include Holstein, Jersey, Ayrshire, Guernsey, and Brown Swiss
Beef: The most popular breeds include Angus, Hereford, Charolais, Simmental, and Chianina; numerous other exist

Normal body temperature

100.5°–102°F (38°–38.8°C)

Respiration

30 breaths per minute

Pulse

Cows: 60–70 beats per minute
Calves: 110–120 beats per minute

Normal hemogram values

Hematocrit: 24%–46%
White blood cells: $4–12 \times 10^3/\mu l$
Total protein: 6–8 g/dl

Breeding information
- **Puberty**

15 months

- **Normal breeding season**

Dairy: all year round
Beef: usually summer

- **Gestation**

279–289 days

- **Estrous cycle**

18–24 days (avg. 21)

- **Duration of estrus**

10–24 hours (avg. 18), ovulation 10–12 hours after end of estrus; cows are bred from midestrus to 6 hours after end of estrus

- **Signs of estrus**

Pacing fence, bawling, riding other cows or standing to be ridden, and clear vaginal discharge.
Bloody vaginal discharge may be seen 2 days postestrus

- **Number of calves**

Usually one, occasionally twins; when twins of unlike sex are born, the female may be an infertile "freemartin"

Neonates

Calves are born with eyes open; calves will usually stand and nurse within a couple of hours

169

	Dairy calves are removed from the dam shortly after birth and are placed on milk replacer for about 6 weeks Beef calves are left with the dam for 6–8 months
Sexing	Males have a pendulous penis and suspended testes, which are descended at birth or within a few days

Vaccinations — Recommendations vary greatly with individual herd situations but may include:
- Leptospirosis
- Infectious bovine rhinotracheitis (IBR)
- Parainfluenza (PI3)
- Bovine viral diarrhea (BVD)
- *Haemophilus*
- *Pasteurella*
- *Clostridium*
- Bovine respiratory syncytial virus (BRSV)
- *Escherichia coli*
- Rotavirus
- Coronavirus
- *Moraxella bovis* (pinkeye)

External parasites — Sarcoptic mange
Lice

Internal parasites — Stomach worms *(Haemonchus, Ostertagia)*
Intestinal worms *(Cooperia, Nematodirus)*
Hookworms *(Bunostomum)*
Threadworms *(Strongyloides)*
Roundworms *(Toxocara)*
Nodular worms *(Oesophagostomum)*
Whipworms *(Trichuris)*
Tapeworms *(Moniezia)*
Coccidia *(Cryptosporidium, Eimeria)*
Liver flukes *(Fasciola)*

Restraint — Tail push, squeeze chute, head gate, stanchion, nose tongs, halter and lead rope

MANAGEMENT GOALS

Good management is very important to the success of a dairy or beef operation. Accurate recordkeeping is essential. All cattle must be ear tagged, tattooed, or otherwise identified. Individual performance and herd performance should be evaluated regularly.

LACTATION PERIODS IN CATTLE

Early	Up to 70 days after calving	Increased milk production
Peak	70–140 days after calving	Decreased milk production
Mid and late	140–305 days after calving	Decreased milk production
Dry period	45–60 days before the next lactation	No milk production

Dairy Cattle

Dairy cattle have been selected for their tremendous capacity to produce milk. They have finer bones and are thinner than beef cattle. Dairy cows produce from between 22 to 99 lb of milk per day—about 15,000 lb per year. Dairy cows are most commonly milked twice a day, but some dairy producers milk three times a day. Milk production peaks around 2 months postpartum and then gradually declines. Optimally, cows are bred back 2 to 3 months after calving.

Two months prior to calving (also called "freshening"), cows are dried off to allow the udder to rest and regenerate. A veterinarian may recommend antibiotic therapy (i.e., "dry cow treatment") to help prevent mastitis during the dry period. Once the cow calves, she is milked and the cycle starts again. Dairy heifers are initially bred at about 15 months and calve by 24 months. They are then introduced into the milking herd. The goal then is one calf per cow per year.

Beef Cattle

Beef cattle are raised for meat production. Beef heifers, like dairy heifers, are bred at 15 months of age. The goal is to produce one calf per cow per year. Beef cattle are usually bred in the summer so that they will calve the next spring, although some are bred to calve in the fall. Beef calves are usually weaned at 6 to 8 months of age.

REPRODUCTION

Heifers should be bred early to improve profitability of the operation. They should be at 65% to 75% of their mature body weight at time of breeding to prevent calving problems. Breeding is done by natural service or by artificial insemination (AI). Most dairies use AI, whereas many beef herds use natural service. AI offers a large genetic pool from which to select, reduces the risk of sexually transmitted diseases, and eliminates the need for keeping a bull. On the other hand, natural service decreases labor costs by eliminating the need for heat detection and catching individual cows to inseminate them. The average heat period in cows is about 8 to 12 hours. With AI cows are bred 12 hours after they have been seen standing to be ridden.

For dairy herds monthly checks should be set up with the veterinarian to monitor herd health and reproduction. Depending on the producer, beef cows may or may not be checked on a yearly basis for pregnancy.

INJECTIONS

Primary intramuscular injection sites include the neck, hip (gluteal muscles), and back of the rear legs (semimembranous, semitendinous muscles). Only 10 ml of solution should be injected at any one site. If the amount exceeds 10 ml, multiple injection sites should be used. Intramuscular injections should be avoided when possible in beef cattle. Subcutaneous injection sites include the neck and over the ribs. Intravenous fluids are administered via the jugular vein. Blood collection sites include the caudal tail vein and the jugular vein. The smallest possible needle size should be used to decrease the amount of tissue damage. For intramuscular or subcutaneous injections an 18 gauge, 1½ inch needle is generally used for cows and a 20 gauge, 1 inch needle for calves. A 14 gauge, 2 inch needle is often used for giving intravenous fluids.

CALF CARE

Calves need colostrum from their mother within 24 hours of birth. A calf's ability to absorb immunoglobulins from colostrum begins to decrease 12 hours after birth and is gone by 24 to 36 hours. Dairy calves are removed from the dam a few days after their birth and fed a good quality milk replacer for about 6 weeks. Calves should begin being offered good quality hay and calf starter grain at 2 weeks of age so that they are eating well by the time they are weaned.

DIET AND FEEDING
Dairy Cattle

Energy and protein are very important components of good nutrition, and requirements for dairy cattle vary depending on the stage of milk production. Good nutrition is most important the first 2 to 3 months after calving, since the cow is producing the most milk at that time and is also recovering from the stress of calving. Specific requirements can be obtained from the National Research Council tables. A variety of grains and forages (i.e., grasses, hays) can be fed. The specific feedstuffs used are not as important as balancing the total ration to meet the cow's requirements. Cows usually receive 40% to 60% of their ration as forages and the remainder as grain. Common ration feedstuffs include alfalfa hay, ear corn or corn silage, rye, soybean meal, orchard grass hay, and cottonseed meal.

During the dry period, cows are fed good quality hay and/or pasture and need little grain. Dry cows should not be fed diets containing a high percentage of corn silage because they will gain too much weight. If cows are too fat at calving, they are more prone to problems such as fatty liver. About 2 weeks before freshening, dry cows and heifers should be fed gradually increasing amounts of grain to avoid digestive problems. After calving, cows should be brought to full feed to help prevent weight loss and energy deficits. Water is a key nutrient, and a fresh, clean source of water should be available at all times.

Beef Cattle

Beef cattle production is most economical when forages are used efficiently. Beef cows are usually offered free-choice forages, such as pasture in the summer and hay and corn fodder in the winter. These forages usually supply all of the nutritional needs of cattle. If forage qual-

DENTAL CHART: CATTLE

Stage	1st Incisor (Middle)	2nd Incisor	3rd Incisor	4th Incisor (Outer)
Adult tooth eruption*	18 months	24 months	36 months	36–48 months
Adult tooth in wear	24 months	30 months		

*Deciduous incisors are present at birth or by 2 months of age.

ity is poor, however, supplemental protein and energy sources will be needed. During lactation nutrient needs of beef cows increase and the cows need better quality hays and silages or even a little grain. Beef calves can also be creep fed, with suckling calves given access to grain mixtures in an enclosure or feeder.

Plenty of fresh water should be available free choice. Beef cows consume more than 3 gallons of water per head per day in the winter and 12 gallons in the summer.

SWINE
DATA CHART

Life span	16 years (avg.); 27 years (max)
Normal body temperature	102° ± 1°F (39°C)
Respiration	20–30 breaths per minute (up to 50 breaths in very young swine, 13–15 breaths in old swine)
Resting pulse	50–80 beats per minute (200 to 280 beats per minute in newborn)
Normal hemogram values	PCV: 40% White blood cells: 11–22 × 10³/µl Total protein: 6–8 g/dl
Breeds	Berkshire Chester white Yorkshire Poland China Duroc American Landrace Hampshire Vietnamese potbellied

Breeding information
- **Puberty**   6–8 months of age for males
5–8 months of age for females
Swine are polyestrus (i.e., the male is no more fertile at one time of year than another; the female will continue to cycle until pregnant)
- **Estrous cycle**   21 days (average)
- **Duration of estrus**   2–3 days with ovulation (release of fertile egg from ovary) occurring 40–46 hours after onset of estrus; it is recommended that the female be bred two times per estrus
- **Signs of estrus**   Swollen vulvar lips, frequent urination in the presence of a boar, acceptance of mating attempts by the boar, and pressure applied to the female's back resulting in "breeding stance" (rigid stance, erect ears)

• **Breeding season**	Year-round
• **Gestation**	114 days (3 months, 3 weeks, 3 days)
• **Litter size**	8–10 piglets born alive
• **Weaning**	6–8 pigs per litter; occurs at 3–6 weeks of age (10–35 lb)

The presence of nursing piglets prevents the sow from cycling, and the sow will enter estrus 4–10 days after its piglets have been weaned

Theoretically, a sow can average 2.57 litters per year (gestation = 114 days, nursing = 21 days, return to service = 7 days)

External parasites
Sarcoptic mange
Lice

Internal parasites
Roundworms *(Ascaris suum)*
Whipworms *(Trichuris suis)*
Threadworms *(Strongyloides)*
Coccidia *(Cryptosporidia, Eimeria,* and *Isospora* spp.)

Vaccinations
Vary with production situation but may include:
• Tetanus
• Leptospirosis
• Transmissible gastroenteritis (TGE)
• *Actinobacillus*
• *Haemophilus*
• *Pasteurella*
• *Clostridium*
• *Escherichia coli*
• Rotavirus
• *Erysipelas*
• Mycoplasma
• *Salmonella*
• *Bordetella* (atrophic rhinitis)

Neonates
Lack of hair makes piglets susceptible to hypothermia, so a warm environment is necessary. Piglets obtain passive antibodies via the sow's colostrum. The tips of the piglets' sharp "needle teeth" may be clipped to reduce trauma to the sow.

Weaning
4 weeks of age

Restraint
Pig-catching gate, leg clamp, snout snare, hobbles, halter and lead

Management goals
Average daily gain = 1.4–1.8 lb/day; it takes approximately 2–2.5 lb of feed to produce 1 lb of pork; approximately 4½–6 months are needed to reach market weight of 215–235 lb

CAPRINE
DATA CHART

Life span	8–12 years	
Breeds	French Alpine	Saanen
	LaMancha	Toggenburg
	Nubian	Angora
	Oberhasli (Swiss Alpine)	African pygmy

Normal body temperature   101.5°–105°F (38.6°–40.5°C)

Respiration   10–30 breaths per minute

Pulse   70–90 beats per minute

Blood collection site   Jugular (may require shearing in wool breeds)

Normal hemogram values   Hematocrit: 28%–35%
White blood cells: $4–13 \times 10^9$/L
Total protein: 6–7.5 g/dl

Breeding information
- **Puberty**   4–12 months
- **Normal breeding season**   Late August to mid-March
- **Estrous cycle**   18–23 days
- **Estrus**   12–36 hours (18 hours avg.); ovulation occurs 12–36 hours after onset of estrus
Does are bred twice daily starting the day after onset of estrus
- **Signs of estrus**   Tail shaking, frequent urination, clear to cloudy mucus discharge, receptive to buck
- **Gestation**   148–153 days
- **Number of kids**   1–3

Neonates   Newborns need colostrum from the doe
"Disbudding" is removal of horn material in the young kid; tattooing is done shortly after birth

Weaning   If the doe's milk is to be used, the kid may be taken away after it has received colostrum and been fed milk replacer
Weaning of kids left with the doe is at 6–12 weeks of age.

Vaccinations   Vary with production situation but may include:
- *Clostridium*
- Tetanus
- Leptospirosis
- *Pasteurella*
- Ecthyma

External parasites	Sarcoptic mange Lice
Internal parasites	Lungworms *(Muellerius, Protostrongylus)* Coccidia *(Cryptosporidium, Eimeria)* Stomach worms *(Ostertagia, Haemonchus)* Intestinal worms *(Trichostrongylus)*
Restraint	Collar or halter and lead, grasp by horns, stanchion
Management goals	Milk goats deliver 4–7 lb of milk per day, with 3.2%–4.5 milk fat Does are dried off 6–8 weeks prior to kidding Angora goats are shorn for their wool (avg. 5.5 lb grease weight of mohair per shearing)

OVINE
DATA CHART

Life span	10–15 years (avg.); 20 years (max.)
Breeds	Rambouillet Suffolk Merino Hampshire Dorset Columbia
Normal body temperature	102°F (38.8°C)
Respiration	19 breaths per minute
Pulse	75 beats per minute
Blood collection sites	Jugular or saphenous vein
Normal hemogram values	PCV: 27%–45% White blood cells: $4–12 \times 10^3/\mu l$ Total protein: 6–7.5 g/dl
Breeding information	
• **Puberty**	9–10 months
• **Breeding season**	Varies with breed; autumn or all year
• **Estrous cycle**	1419 days (avg. 17)
• **Estrus**	24–48 hours; ovulation is near end of estrus Should be bred beginning 18 hours after onset of estrus or ewes can be left with ram
• **Signs of estrus**	Receptive to ram
• **Gestation**	144–151 days
• **Number of lambs**	1–3
Neonates	Newborns must be dried, kept warm, and fed colostrum Tails may be docked and males castrated during the first week

Weaning	1–6 months of age, depending on producer
Vaccinations	See Caprine Data Chart
Parasites	See Caprine Data Chart
Restraint	Gates and hurdles, hold sheep with one arm around rump and one arm around head
Management goals	Sheep are bred for meat and wool; those bred for meat should average 1.5 lambs per ewe per year Shearing is done in late spring

OSTRICH
DATA CHART

Life span	20–30 years in the wild, longer in captivity
Normal body temperature	102.2°–105°F (39°–40.5°C)
Respiration	6–12 breaths per minute
Pulse	120 beats per minute
Weight	Males: 150 kg Females: 100–130 kg
Blood collection sites	Brachial vein, jugular vein (right larger than left), medial metatarsal vein (in anesthetized birds)
Diet	Requirements still under investigation Commercial ratite chow must provide 16%–20% protein (18% better), ≤10% fat, ≤10% fiber, ~2.5% calcium, ~1.5% phosphorus; supplement with vitamin E and selenium when necessary
Common diseases	Omphalitis, yolk sacculitis, air sacculitis, sinusitis, enteritis in chicks, egg abnormalities, embryonic malformation, long bone deviation, porosis, scoliosis, kyphosis, egg binding, infectious metritis, enteritis (viral and bacterial), disease resulting from foreign body ingestion and proventricular impaction Trauma to legs Endoparasites and ectoparasites ("eye flukes": *Philophthalmus gralli*)
Breeding information	
• Sexual maturity	2 years; males become productive breeders at 3–5 years; females lay eggs at 2–3 years

- **Clutch size**
- **Incubation**

	16–23 eggs laid within 2 weeks
	40–42 days (up to 45 days)
	Egg weight loss during incubation 14%
	Temperature and humidity control are important

- **Breeding behavior**

Males exhibit brighter colors on neck and legs
Ritual synchronized "dancing"
Vocalization (male)

Neonates

Swab navel with dilute iodine solution
Keep chicks in hatcher 24–48 hours after hatching
Keep in brooder box for 2–3 weeks in groups of 6 or
    less, then move to the brooder pen
Chicks will not eat for the first 2–5 days

Sexing

Manual eversion of cloaca
Males: Phallus with dorsal spermatic groove and
    cartilaginous matrix
Females: Clitoral structure with dorsal pale pink
    margin; no groove or cartilage
Chromosomal analysis
Sexual dimorphism: Males 15–20 months of age will
    have black and white feathers; females will remain
    brown gray

Miscellaneous

Use strict hygiene measures during incubation and
    neonatal periods
All pens must be clean of debris and small rocks to
    prevent foreign body ingestion

RHEA
DATA CHART

Life span	20–25 years
Normal body temperature	102.2°–104°F (39°–40°C)
Respiration	12–15 breaths per minute
Pulse	120–130 beats per minute
Weight	20–25 kg
Blood collection sites	Brachial vein
	Jugular vein (right larger than left)
Diet	Requirements still under investigation
	Commercial ratite chow must provide 16%–20% protein (18% better), ≤10% fat, ≤10% fiber, ~2.5% calcium, ~0.5% phosphorus; supplement with vitamin E and selenium when necessary

Common diseases	Egg binding, infectious metritis, egg abnormalities, embryonic malformation, omphalitis, yolk sacculitis, air sacculitis, sinusitis, enteritis in chicks, long bone deviation, porosis, scoliosis, kyphosis, endoparasites and ectoparasites, trauma to legs, enteritis (viral and bacterial), disease resulting from foreign body ingestion, and proventricular impaction

Breeding information
- **Sexual maturity**
- **Clutch size**
- **Incubation**

- **Breeding behavior**

2 years
18 eggs (avg.)
35–40 days
Temperatures and humidity control are important
Egg weight loss during incubation 14%
Increased aggressiveness and vocalization ("nan-du") by males

Neonates

Swab navel with dilute iodine solution
Keep chicks in hatcher 24–48 hours after hatching
Keep in brooder box for 2–3 weeks in groups of 6 or less, then move to brooder pen
Chicks will not eat for the first 2–5 days

Sexing

Manual eversion of cloaca
Chromosomal analysis
Sexual dimorphism: males have darker plumage on neck and chest

Miscellaneous

Use strict hygiene during incubation and neonatal periods
All pens must be clear of debris and small rocks to prevent foreign body ingestion

AVIAN CARE

BUDGERIGAR
(Melopsittacus undulatus)
DATA CHART

Life span	8–15 years
Normal body temperature	105°–107°F (40.5°–41.6°C)
Respiration	80–100 breaths per minute
Weight	30–40 g
Blood collection sites	Jugular vein, wing vein, toenail; a blood sample representing 1% of the body weight can be safely taken
Diet	Commercial pelleted diet with green and yellow vegetables, fruits, and sprouts A limited amount of seed is best
Common diseases	Malnutrition, fatty liver, bumblefoot, renal and ovarian neoplasia, cnemidocoptic mange, lipomas, gram-negative bacterial infections
Breeding information	
• **Puberty**	6–8 months
• **Breeding season**	All year; 3 clutches per year
• **Eggs per clutch**	5–10
• **Incubation period**	16 days
• **Breeding**	Male (cock) sings for longer periods and regurgitates to the female (hen); the pair copulates daily for several days The hen lays one egg every other day beginning 1 week after mating; the cock feeds the hen when she begins incubating the eggs
Neonates	Eyes open 7 days following hatching Fledge at 4 weeks Wean at 6 weeks
Sex determination	Cock has blue cere (fleshy area above the beak); hen has a beige or tan cere that turns dark brown during breeding season

181

Miscellaneous	Budgerigars are commonly called budgies or parakeets; however, they are not true parakeets
	Budgerigars will talk
	Budgerigars require nesting boxes for brooding

PARROT
DATA CHART

Life span	Greater than 40 years
Varieties	The most popular pet parrots are African Grey (*Psittacus erithacus*) and Amazon (*Amazona* spp.) parrots
Normal body temperature	105°–107°F (40.5°–41.6°C)
Respiration and pulse	Variable
Environmental temperature	40°–80°F (4.4°–26.6°C)
Weight	African Greys (370–530 g)
	Amazons (350–1000 g), depending on the species
Blood collection sites	Wing vein, right jugular vein, medial metatarsal vein; the volume of blood that can be safely collected from a sick bird is 1% of the body weight or less
Diet	Commercial pelleted diet with green and yellow vegetables, fruits, sprouts, occasional cooked egg, and small amounts of meat and cheese; limited amount of seeds
Common diseases	Pox, respiratory diseases/sinusitis, chlamydiosis, hypovitaminosis A, aspergillosis, hypocalcemia, seizures (African Greys), feather picking, gram-negative bacterial infections
Breeding information	
• Puberty	Breeding age for most parrots is 4–6 years
• Breeding season	Spring-summer
• Incubation	Amazons: 23–24 days
	African Greys: 24–26 days
• Eggs per clutch	2–4, laid every other day
Neonates	Hatched naked and helpless
	Fledge at 45–60 days
	Wean at 90–120 days
Sex determination	Parrots must be surgically or genetically sexed
Miscellaneous	Parrots tend to be aggressive during the breeding season
	Parrots are prone to feather picking

Amazons are noisy in early morning and late
  evening
Amazon and African Grey parrots can be good
  talkers

CANARY
(Serinus canarias)
DATA CHART

Life span	5–15 years
Varieties	Numerous hybrids genetically selected for color, singing ability (Border), fluffy feathers (Frill)
Normal body temperature	105°–107°F (40.5°–41.6°C)
Respiration and pulse	Variable
Environmental temperature	40°–80°F (4.4°–26.6°C)
Weight	12–30 g
Blood collection sites	Right jugular vein, toenail; the volume of blood that can be safely collected from a bird is 1% of the body weight
Diet	Canary seed mix, green and yellow vegetables, sprouts, hard-cooked egg, whole grain bread, cuttlebone, mineral block
Common diseases	Obesity, cnemidocoptic mange, respiratory mites, canary pox, feather cysts, cataracts, overgrowth of nails
Breeding information	
• Puberty	1 year of age
• Breeding season	Spring; 3–4 clutches per year
• Incubation	13–14 days
• Eggs per clutch	4–6; eggs laid every other day
• Signs of estrus	Hen calls and is receptive to cock
Neonates	Hatched naked and helpless Fledge at 14 days Wean at 18–21 days First molt at 8 weeks
Sex determination	Males sing louder and with greater vigor than females
Miscellaneous	Canaries are messy eaters Molting occurs July through October, lasting 6–8 weeks Require cup-shaped nests or half-open nest boxes

COCKATIEL
(Nymphicus hollandicus)
DATA CHART

Life span	15–25 years
Varieties	Albino, lutino, pied, cinnamon, gray, fallow, charcoal, white-faced
Normal body temperature	105°–107°F (40.5°–41.6°C)
Respiration and pulse	Variable
Environmental temperature	40°–80°F (4.4°–26.6°C)
Weight	75–100 g
Blood collection sites	Right jugular vein, wing vein, medial metatarsal vein, toenail; the volume of blood that can be safely collected from a bird is 1% of its body weight
Diet	Commercial pelleted diet is ideal; cockatiel seed mix, dark green and yellow vegetables, whole grain bread, fruit, mineral block, cuttlebone
Common diseases	Conjunctivitis, feather picking, egg binding, *Giardia* infection, hepatic lipidosis, chronic egg laying
Breeding information	
• **Puberty**	7–12 months
• **Breeding season**	All year
• **Incubation**	18–21 days, both sexes incubate eggs
• **Eggs per clutch**	4–7; eggs laid every other day
• **Signs of estrus**	Hen receptive to cock
Neonates	Hatched naked and helpless
	Fledge at 32–38 days
	Wean at 47–52 days
	First molt at 6 months
Sex determination	Adult males have a solid-colored tail and yellow face, whereas females have yellow bars on the ventral surface of the tail and primary feathers and less yellow on the face; sex determination is difficult in some varieties
Miscellaneous	Cockatiels are good whistlers
	Good choice for a first bird

MACAW
(*Ara* spp.)
DATA CHART

Life span	Greater than 40 years
Varieties	Large and small species; Blue and Gold, Scarlet, Green-winged, Noble, Severe, and Yellow-collared are the most common
Normal body temperature	105°–107°F (40.5°–41.6°C)
Respiration and pulse	Variable
Environmental temperature	40°–80°F (4.4°–26.6°C)
Weight	Large macaws: 800–1600 g Small macaws: 250–500 g
Blood collection sites	Wing vein, right jugular vein, medial metatarsal vein; the volume of blood that can be safely collected from a bird is 1% of its body weight
Diet	Commercial pelleted diet with green and yellow vegetables, sprouts, fruit, occasional cooked egg, and a small amount of meat and cheese; limited amount of seed
Common diseases	Feather picking, proventricular dilatation syndrome (macaw wasting disease), herpesvirus depigmentation on feet, feather cysts, papillomatosis, chlamydiosis, gram-negative bacterial infections
Breeding information	
• **Puberty**	Breeding age (large macaws): 5–7 years Breeding age (small macaws): 4–6 years
• **Breeding season**	Spring-summer
• **Incubation**	Large macaws: 26–28 days Small macaws: 23–24 days
• **Eggs per clutch**	2–4
Neonates	Hatched naked and helpless Fledge: 70–80 days (large macaws); 45–60 days (small macaws) Wean: 120–150 days (large macaws); 90–120 days (small macaws)
Sex determination	Macaws must be surgically or genetically sexed
Miscellaneous	Macaws are noisy, especially at dawn and dusk Macaws can be extremely aggressive during breeding season, can be destructive to immediate environment

COCKATOO
(*Cacatua* spp.)
DATA CHART

Life span	Greater than 40 years
Varieties	The most common pet cockatoos are Moluccan, Umbrella, Medium Sulfur-crested, Citron-crested, Goffins, and Bare-eyed
Normal body temperature	105°–107°F (40.5°–41.6°C)
Respiration and pulse	Variable
Environmental temperature	40°–80°F (4.4°–26.6°C)
Weight	Moluccan: 650–1000 g Umbrella: 450–700 g Medium Sulfur-crested and Citron-crested: 430–510 g Bare-eyed: 300–500 g
Blood collection sites	Wing vein, right jugular vein, medial metatarsal vein; the volume of blood that can be safely collected from a bird is 1% of its body weight or less
Diet	Commercial pelleted diet with green and yellow vegetables, sprouts, fruit, occasional cooked egg, and small amounts of meat and cheese; limited amount of seeds
Common diseases	Psittacine beak and feather disease, feather picking, herpesvirus papillomas on feet, gram-negative bacterial infections
Breeding information	
• **Puberty**	Medium cockatoos: 3–4 years Large cockatoos: 5–6 years
• **Breeding season**	Spring-summer
• **Eggs per clutch**	2–4
• **Incubation period**	Medium cockatoos: 23–25 days Large cockatoos: 24–26 days
Neonates	Hatched naked and helpless Fledge: 45–60 days (medium cockatoos); 60–80 days (large cockatoos) Wean: 90–120 days (medium cockatoos); 120–150 days (large cockatoos)
Sex determination	Surgically or genetically sexed; the eyes of adult females of some species may be red-brown, whereas the males have black eyes

Miscellaneous   Cockatoos are easily stressed
                              Have an abundant amount of "powder down"
                              Can be very noisy, especially Moluccans

FINCH
DATA CHART

Life span	5–15 years
Varieties	Many species, primarily from Australia; Zebra finch (*Taeniopygia guttatta*) and Society finch (*Lonchura stiata*) are the most popular
Normal body temperature	105°–107°F (40.5°–41.6°C)
Respiration and pulse	Variable
Environmental temperature	40°–80°F (4.4°–26.6°C)
Weight	10–16 g
Blood collection sites	Right jugular vein, toenail; the volume of blood that can be safely collected from a bird is 1% of its body weight
Diet	Finch seed mix, fruits, green and yellow vegetables, sprouts, hard-cooked egg, whole grain bread, cuttlebone, mineral block; some species require insects
Common diseases	Parasites (air sac mites, proventricular nematodes), pox, egg-binding, malnutrition
Breeding information	
• **Puberty**	6–9 months (Zebra finch)
• **Breeding season**	Year-round (Zebra finch)
• **Incubation**	13–16 days (Zebra finch)
• **Eggs per clutch**	4–5 (Zebra finch)
• **Signs of estrus**	Hens receptive to cock
Neonates	Hatched naked and helpless Wean at 20–22 days (Zebra finch)
Sex determination	Male Zebra finches have orange-red ear spots, beak, and legs, whereas the females lack ear spots and have less red in the beak and legs
Miscellaneous	Zebra finches are prolific breeders and will continue to construct nests over eggs if excessive nesting material is not removed after the first clutch is laid

PIGEON AND DOVE
DATA CHART

Life span	5–15 years
Varieties	Over 300 species of pigeons and doves; domestic pigeons (*Columba livia*) and Ringdove (*Streptopelia risoria*) are the most common
Normal body temperature	105°–107°F (40.5°–41.6°C)
Respiration and pulse	Variable
Environmental temperature	Domestic pigeons tolerate a wide temperature range
Weight	Most adult pigeons weigh 350–550 g
Blood collection sites	Right jugular vein, wing vein, medial metatarsal vein; the volume of blood that can be safely collected from a bird is 1% of its body weight
Diet	Commercial pigeon and dove diet, mixed grains Pigeons consume 30–40 g feed per day and 30–50 ml water per day
Common diseases	Chlamydiosis, trichomoniasis, salmonellosis, pigeonpox, *Tetrameres* infection, paramyxovirus, pigeon herpesvirus
Breeding information	
• **Puberty**	4 months (pigeons)
• **Breeding season**	Spring-summer
• **Incubation**	17 days
• **Eggs per clutch**	2 (average)
• **Signs of estrus**	Hen receptive to cock
Neonates	Pigeon squabs are fed regurgitated secretions called "crop milk"
Sex determination	Males are more vocal than females and exhibit courtship displays; pigeons and doves can be surgically sexed
Miscellaneous	Pigeons and doves have no gallbladder Pigeons and doves have paired ceca Pigeons and doves are able to drink water without elevating the head and extending the neck

MYNAH
DATA CHART

Life span	Greater than 10 years
Varieties	Hill mynah (*Gracula religiosa*) is most common

Normal body temperature	105°–107°F (40.5°–41.6°C)
Respiration and pulse	Variable
Environmental temperature	50°–80°F (10°–26.6°C)
Weight	400–500 g
Blood collection sites	Wing vein, right jugular vein, medial metatarsal vein; the volume of blood that can be safely collected from a bird is 1% or less of its body weight
Diet	Commercial formulated diets (limited iron content), fruits, vegetables, cooked egg
Common diseases	Iron storage disease, liver cirrhosis, chronic active hepatitis, gram-negative bacterial infections
Breeding information	
• **Puberty**	1–2 years
• **Breeding season**	Spring-summer
• **Incubation**	14–16 days
• **Eggs per clutch**	2–3
Neonates	Hatched naked and helpless Fledge at 1 month Wean at 2 months
Sex determination	Surgical sexing
Miscellaneous	Mynahs remain aloof and do not like to be handled or touched They have excellent mimicry and vocalize constantly They have very loose, messy droppings

ORPHAN BIRDS

Altricial wild birds, such as raptors, songbirds, pigeons, and doves, are hatched naked, blind, and helpless. As orphans, these species require immediate critical care to survive. In comparison, precocial birds, such as chickens, ducks, quail, and turkeys, hatch fully feathered and are able to consume food and water immediately.

Altricial Orphans
Emergency Care

Hypothermic chicks should be warmed in an incubator or with a heat lamp set to provide a 95° to 100°F (35° to 37.7°C) environment. Dehydrated chicks should be given oral or subcutaneous fluids; those that are hypoglycemic are given an oral or injectable glucose solution.

Environment

During the first 7 to 14 days of life, chicks (i.e., songbirds) should be placed in an environment with the surrounding air heated to 80° to 90°F (26.6° to 32.2°C) and the chick placed on a warm (i.e., 90°F) surface such as a heating pad. Chicks do best if the humidity is kept above 50% relative humidity. Below 30% relative humidity, chicks become dehydrated. Chicks should be placed in small containers lined with cloth diapers or indoor-outdoor carpeting to provide support and facilitate cleaning. After 2 weeks of age when chicks are feathered with down, the temperature can be gradually reduced to 80° to 85°F (26.6° to 29.4°C). When fully feathered, chicks can be moved to an open cage in a room heated to 70° to 80°F (21.1° to 26.6°C).

Diets for Nestling Birds

Commercially prepared diets designed for hand-raising pet psittacine birds can be used to raise most wild orphan granivore and omnivore altricial chicks. Also, a diet can be prepared to feed a variety of granivore, omnivore, and insectivore chicks; the diet consists of 1 cup water, softened high protein dog food or pablum, ½ cup mynah or turkey pellets, 2 soft-boiled eggs, ⅓ cup cooked Roman meal cereal, 1 teaspoon dark loam, and 1 teaspoon powdered avian vitamin and mineral mix. Earthworms, live insects, and dried insect food (i.e., fish food) should be added to the diet of insectivores, such as robins, swallows, mockingbirds, finches, nighthawks, crows, and blackbirds. Hawk and owl chicks are fed minced, skinned rodents or plucked day-old cockerels or quail rolled in bone meal for the first 2 to 10 days; thereafter the fur or feathers can be fed. When the birds are casting well, they can be fed whole prey items.

Methods of Feeding

Forceps, toothpicks, 1 to 3 ml syringes with the needle adaptor removed, or feeding tubes can be used to feed orphan chicks. Healthy chicks should be fed following stimulation of the food-begging reflex. Force feeding should be performed only on weak chicks. Chicks with crops should be fed amounts and frequencies that allow the crop to be

DETERMINATION OF THE AGE OF ALTRICIAL CHICKS	
1 week	Naked
2 weeks	Pinfeathers over most of the skin
3 weeks	Fully feathered, unable to fly
4–6 weeks	Able to fly

one-half to three-quarters full most of the day. The following feeding schedule works well for songbird chicks:

Day 0–4	Feed every 10–15 minutes from 6:00 A.M.–10:00 P.M.
Day 4–10	Feed every 15–20 minutes from 6:00 A.M.–10:00 P.M.
Day 10–14	Feed every 45–60 minutes from 6:30 A.M.–9:30 P.M.
Day 15+	Feed every 60–90 minutes from 7:00 A.M.–9:00 P.M.

Precocial Orphans
Emergency Care
Emergency treatment of precocial chicks is the same as that described for altricial chicks.

Environment
Orphan precocial chicks should be placed in an incubator, brooder, or small cardboard box that contains several holes for ventilation. The environmental temperature should be kept at 90° to 95°F (32.2° to 35°C) for the first week of life. The temperature should be lowered by 5° each week until a minimum of 75°F (23.8°C) is reached. Water is best provided in a self-watering device; for the first week, pebbles should be placed in the water pans to prevent drowning.

Diet
A commercial poultry or gamebird starter mash or crumbles should be fed free choice until the bird is 3 weeks of age, at which time grit and chicken scratch are added to the diet. Older birds can be maintained on scratch and a balanced, milled poultry or gamebird ration.

Release to the Wild
At 12 weeks of age, the orphan bird should be ready to be released.

Bibliography

Bulger D: *All About Breeding Cockatiels.* Neptune, TFH Publications, 1983.

Evans RH: Care and feeding of orphan mammals and birds, in Kirk RW (ed): *Current Veterinary Therapy IX, Small Animal Practice.* Philadelphia, WB Saunders, 1986, pp 775–787.

Gallerstein GA: *Bird Owner's Home Health and Care Handbook.* New York, Howell Book House Inc, 1984.

Harrison GJ, Harrison LR: *Clinical Avian Medicine and Surgery.* Philadelphia, WB Saunders, 1986.

Practical Avian Medicine. Trenton, NJ, Veterinary Learning Systems, 1997.

Ritchie BW, Harrison GJ, Harrison LR (eds): *Avian Medicine: Principles and Application.* Lake Worth, FL, Wingers Publishing, 1994.

Roberts MF: *All About Breeding Canaries.* Neptune, TFH Publications, 1982.

Techniques in Avian Medicine: Parts 1 and 2 (video). Trenton, NJ, Veterinary Learning Systems, 1993.

Vriends MM: *Simon and Schuster's Guide to Pet Birds.* New York, Simon and Schuster, 1984.

Wages DP: Diseases of pigeons. *Vet Clin North Am Small Anim Pract* 17(5): 1089–1107, 1987.

OTHER
EXOTIC ANIMALS

FRESHWATER AND MARINE FISH
DATA CHART

Life span   Variable; goldfish can live up to 25 years

Blood collection sites   Caudal vein (insert a 22-gauge needle into the
                             ventral midline of the peduncle until a vertebra
                             stops the needle, then withdraw the needle until
                             blood is aspirated into the syringe)
                             Not practical for fish less than 10 g

Water requirements
• Freshwater fish   Optimum water pH: 6.5–7.5 depending on the
                             species
                             Optimum aeration: 1.5–2 L of air per hour
                             (concentration more than 5 ppm)
                             Water ammonia levels should be less than 0.02 ppm,
                             water NO_2 level should be less than 0.1 ppm,
                             and water NO_3 level should be less than 100 ppm
                             Water temperature should be 65°–72°F (18°–22°C) for
                             goldfish and 76°–80°F (24°–27°C) for tropical fish
                             To remove harmful chlorine from municipal water
                             supplies, aerate water for several days or use
                             sodium thiosulfate
                             Maximum carrying capacity in a home aquarium is 1
                             inch of fish for each 10 square inches of surface
                             water or 1 inch of fish per gallon of water
• Marine fish   Natural seawater or commercial seawater mix,
                             optimum pH 8.1 to 8.3, optimum salinity of 35 ppt
                             Water NO_3 should be less than 50 ppm
                             Other parameters the same as for freshwater fish

Diet   Commercial diets are available for different species
                             of fish
                             Feed only the amount the fish will consume in 5
                             minutes
                             Feed adults twice a day and young three times a day

Common diseases
• Freshwater fish   Gram-negative bacterial infections, tuberculosis,

monogenetic trematodes, lymphocystis, disease caused by *Ichthyophthirius* (Ich), ammonia toxicity (new tank syndrome)

- **Marine fish**
Gram-negative bacterial infections, disease caused by *Cryptocaryon*, protozoal diseases (ciliates, flagellates, and microsporidia), trematodes, nematodes

Breeding information (goldfish)
- **Breeding season**
Spring; a cool period followed by warming triggers breeding in goldfish

- **Eggs per spawn**
Variable depending on species; up to 10,000
- **Incubation period**
5–7 days; goldfish fry hatch and hang onto plants by sticky head glands for 48–72 hours before swimming off to forage for food

- **Breeding behavior**
Male goldfish chases the female and pushes her against plants while both fish gyrate from side to side and eject eggs and sperm into the water; the eggs stick to plants during incubation

Spawning takes 2 to 3 hours

Adults may consume the eggs if not removed from the area immediately following completion of spawning

Sex determination (goldfish)
Male goldfish develop white pimple-like bumps (breeding tubercles) on the head and gills during the breeding season; females will appear swollen with eggs

SNAKE
(order Squamata, suborder Serpentes)
DATA CHART

Life span
8–60 years depending on the species

Varieties
The species most commonly kept as pets include boas, king snakes, rat snakes, Burmese pythons, and reticulated pythons

Size
Length may range from 60 cm to greater than 1000 cm (pythons)

Environmental temperature
Temperate species: 73°–82°F (23°–28°C)
Tropical species: 79°–86°F (26°–30°C)

Blood collection sites
Caudal vein, palatine veins, cardiac puncture

Diet
Snakes are carnivores; the prey is eaten whole
Most pet snakes will accept dead prey
The diet depends on the species but includes invertebrates (insects, worms), fish, birds, amphibians, mammals, and eggs

The smaller species require food every day, while larger snakes eat once every 7–14 days

Common diseases

Gram-negative bacterial sepsis, nutritional deficiencies, necrotic stomatitis, respiratory disease, mite and tick infestation, intestinal parasites, abnormal ecdysis (skin shedding)

Breeding information
• **Puberty**

Small species: Less than 1 year
Large species: 1–3 years

• **Breeding season**

Spring-summer

• **Gestation**

Boas, water snakes, and most vipers are viviparous (bear live young)
The gestation period in boa constrictors is 6 months
Most other snakes are egg layers; the incubation period varies with the species, (e.g., 70 days in rat snakes, 65–70 days in pythons)

• **Litter size**

Boas produce 20–60 young at parturition, whereas oviparous snakes may lay 10 (rat snakes) to 100 (pythons) eggs per clutch, depending on the species

• **Signs of estrus**

During the breeding season, females secrete pheromones from glands in the skin to attract males; a male will rub his chin along the back of a receptive female

Neonates

Abandoned by the parents at birth, neonates do not eat until they have completed their first ecdysis, which occurs 4–10 days after birth or hatching

Sex determination

In some species the male has a gradually tapering tail, whereas the female has an abruptly constricted tail
Probing of the hemipenes via the cloacal vent in a caudal direction is a common method to determine the sex of snakes; male boas and pythons have paired paracloacal "spurs"

Miscellaneous

Snakes have a distinct cycle of ecdysis, which is affected by age, nutrition, size, and temperature: First the eyes and skin become milky blue (4–7 days) and then the eyes and skin clear; this is followed by shedding 4–7 days later
Venomous species are examined in plexiglass tubes or while under a general anesthetic
Injections with potentially nephrotoxic drugs should be given in the cranial half of the snake to avoid the renal portal system.
Snakes kept in their optimum temperature zone and fed a proper diet have fewer health problems;

ambient temperature has a marked effect on the
metabolism of drugs given to reptiles, so it is
particularly important to maintain snakes in their
optimum temperature range during treatment

LIZARD
(Order Squamata, suborder Sauria)
DATA CHART

Life span	Variable depending on species
Varieties	2900 species; green iguanas, leopard geckos, and anoles are common pet lizards
Environmental temperature	Temperate species (e.g., anoles): 73°–82°F (23°–28°C)
	Tropical species (e.g., iguanas): 79°–86° F (26°–30°C)
Blood collection sites	Caudal vein, orbital sinus
Diet	Lizards may be herbivorous, carnivorous, omnivorous, or have highly specialized dietary requirements; commercial reptile diets are available
	Young iguanas are more omnivorous than adults and will occasionally eat eggs, insects, or mouse pups
	Adult iguanas eat a variety of vegetables and fruits; anoles and geckos are mostly insectivorous
Common diseases	Metabolic bone disease, respiratory infections, gram-negative bacterial infections
Breeding information	
• **Puberty**	Small species: less than 1 year
	Larger lizards: 1–3 years
• **Breeding season**	Spring-summer
• **Gestation**	Under natural conditions gecko and iguana eggs hatch in 47–50 days
• **Signs of estrus**	Female allows male to mount
Neonates	Abandoned by parents at hatch, hatchlings may not eat until after their first shed
Sex determination	In some species the male is more brightly colored
	Male iguanas have distinct femoral pores; male geckos have distinct pores cranial to the cloaca
	Probing of the hemipenes may be useful in some species
Miscellaneous	Lizards kept in their optimum temperature zone and fed a proper diet have fewer health problems

TURTLE
(Order Chelonia)
DATA CHART

Life span	50–130 years in some species
Varieties	Turtles, tortoises, and terrapins; the most common pet species are painted turtles, sliders, box turtles, leopard tortoises, and red-footed tortoises
Blood collection sites	Caudal vein, jugular vein
Diet	Box turtles eat meats, insects, worms, dog food, flowers, fruits, and vegetables Tortoises are herbivorous, whereas semiaquatic turtles are omnivorous A wide variety of foods should be fed to minimize the chances of nutritional deficiencies Commercial reptile diets are available
Common diseases	Hypovitaminosis A, pneumonia, shell trauma, metabolic bone disease
Breeding information	
• **Puberty**	10–20 years depending on the species
• **Breeding season**	Spring; eggs laid in the summer of same year
• **Eggs per clutch**	4–12
• **Incubation period**	2–3 months (temperature dependent)
Sex determination	Sexual dimorphism is dramatic in some species and minimal in others Young turtles are difficult to sex In some aquatic species, males are smaller than females and have long claws on the front feet Adult male tortoises have a concave plastron, whereas females have a flat plastron The tails of male turtles may be longer than those of females
Miscellaneous	Turtles kept in their optimum temperature zone and fed a proper diet have fewer health problems Turtles, like all reptiles, may carry *Salmonella*, a potentially zoonotic bacterium Tortoises are strictly terrestrial, whereas turtles and terrapins are more aquatic Ivermectin is potentially toxic to turtles and tortoises and should not be used

GERBIL
(Meriones unguiculatus)
DATA CHART

Life span	2–4 years
Varieties	Agouti, light brown to white, color variants, black and gray mutants
Normal body temperature	96°–103°F (36°–39°C)
Respiration	70–120 breaths per minute (90 avg.)
Pulse	260–600 per minute (360 avg.)
Weight	65–120 g; males are slightly larger
Blood collection	Orbital sinus, caudal vein, heart
Diet	Pelleted rodent diet or a combination of mixed grains and seeds with 22% protein Feed can be supplemented with occasional sunflower seed Adults eat 5–7 g of feed per day
Common diseases	Dermatitis (facial, sore nose), demodectic mange, epileptiform seizures, chronic interstitial nephritis, cystic ovaries, enteritis, neoplasia
Breeding information	
• **Puberty**	9–12 weeks
• **Gestation**	24–26 days
• **Litter size**	4–7
• **Signs of estrus**	Restlessness, congested vulva
Neonates	Naked and blind at birth Wean at 25–35 days
Sex determination	The distance between the anus and the genital orifice is greater in males (10 mm) than it is in females (5 mm) Males have a dark-colored scrotum
Miscellaneous	Incisor teeth continue to grow throughout the lifetime of the animal Gerbils are naturally lipemic, odor free, and monogamous; they mate for life and rarely bite Gerbils have large adrenal glands

GUINEA PIG
(Cavia porcellus)
DATA CHART

Life span	4–5 years
Varieties	English (short-haired, smooth coat) Abyssinian (short, wired hair) Peruvian (long-haired, silky coat) Angora
Normal body temperature	100°–103°F (37°–39°C)
Respirations	90–150 breaths per minute
Pulse	230–320 per minute
Weight	Males (boars): 900–1200 g Females (sows): 700–900 g
Blood collection sites	Orbital sinus, cranial vena cava, femoral artery or vein, toenail
Diet	Commercial pelleted guinea pig food (18%–20% protein, 4% fat, 16% fiber) and fresh cabbage, kale, hay, and fruit Guinea pigs are herbivores and require 20 mg/kg vitamin C daily
Common diseases	Cervical lymphadenitis, pododermatitis, bacterial pneumonia, otitis media, dermatophytosis (*Trichophyton mentagrophytes*), sarcoptic mange (*Trixacarus caviae*), scorbutus, antibiotic-associated enterocolitis, pregnancy toxemia, dental disorders
Breeding information	
• **Puberty**	Males: 600–700 g (3–4 months) Females: 350–450 g (2–3 months)
• **Breeding season**	Polyestrus; 3–5 litters per year
• **Gestation**	58–72 days (68 avg.)
• **Average litter size**	3–4
Signs of estrus	Sow demonstrates the position of lordosis to the boar. A vaginal mucus plug indicates that the sow has been bred
Neonates	Born fully haired with eyes open, able to eat food immediately; birth weight 60–100 g Wean at 2–3 weeks
Sex determination	Male's penis will extrude when the abdomen is pressed; females have a U-shaped vaginal orifice covered by a membrane between the urethral and anal orifices

Miscellaneous	Guinea pigs do not have tails
	All teeth continue to grow throughout the lifetime of the animal
	Guinea pigs ingest soft fecal pellets (cecotrophs), which are high in protein, vitamins, and minerals

HAMSTER
(Mesocricetus auratus)
DATA CHART

Life span	2–4 years
Varieties	Syrian (golden) most common, Chinese (striped back), Armenian (gray), and European
Normal body temperature	98°–101°F (37°–39°C)
Respirations	40–120 breaths per minute (75 avg.)
Pulse	250–600 per minute (450 avg.)
Weight	100–150 g; female slightly larger than male
Blood collection sites	Orbital sinus, heart, or anterior vena cava
Diet	Commercial rat or mouse diet, hamster seed mixes, vegetables, fruit, hay, chopped meat, dog biscuits, mealworms, live insects
	Adults eat 5–7 g feed per day
Common diseases	Proliferative ileitis (wet tail), abscesses (e.g., caused by *Staphylococcus*), demodicosis, lymphocytic choriomeningitis, dental disorders, generalized amyloidosis, neoplasms
Breeding information	
• **Puberty**	4–5 weeks
• **Gestation**	16–18 days
• **Litter size**	4–10 pups
• **Signs of estrus**	Viscous, white to yellow vaginal discharge 3 days prior to heat; lordosis
Neonates	Eyes open at 12 days
	Wean at 3–4 weeks
Sex determination	The anal-genital distance is greater in the male than in the female; males have an os penis
Miscellaneous	Hamsters have cheek pouches and short tails, are nocturnal, and are clean and odor free
	Hamsters will bite, are prone to antibiotic-associated colitis, and can be cannibalistic

RABBIT
(Oryctolagus cuniculus)
DATA CHART

Life span	5–10 years
Varieties	Greater than 50 breeds; common breeds include the New Zealand white, Californian, Dutch, Florida white, Flemish, Rex, Dutch belted, and Netherlands dwarf
Normal body temperature	103°F (39.5°C)
Respirations	35–65 breaths per minute
Pulse	120–300 per minute
Blood collection sites	Ear veins, heart
Diet	Commercial rabbit pellets (15%–19% protein, 16%–29% fiber), quality hay Rabbits eat 116–127 g of food per day Rabbits ingest the soft fecal pellets (cecotrophs), which are produced at night; cecotrophs are high in protein, minerals, and B vitamins
Common diseases	Pasteurellosis, venereal spirochetosis, tularemia, enteropathies, ear mites (*Psoroptes cuniculi*), cuterebriasis, ulcerative dermatitis, posterior paresis/paralysis (lumbar spine fractures), hairballs
Breeding information	
• **Puberty**	Male (buck): 6–7 months Female (doe): 5–6 months
• **Breeding season**	Spring-late summer
• **Gestation**	31–32 days
• **Litter size**	4–10
• **Signs of estrus**	Doe has a swollen, reddened vulva and stands to be mounted Receptivity is determined by confining the doe with the buck for 5–30 minutes; if doe is receptive and buck experienced, copulation usually occurs rapidly
Neonates	Immature at birth, poikilothermic for first 7 days or more; nurse only once a day Wean at 5–8 weeks (480–640 g)
Sex determination	The male's penis will protrude when the area above the genital opening is pressed Both sexes have dewlaps Bucks have no nipples and hairless scrotal sacs; does have 8–12 nipples

Miscellaneous

When restraining a conscious rabbit, its hindquarters should be supported to avoid injury to the animal's back if it struggles

Cat bags and restraint boxes can be used to restrain rabbits

Rabbits will scratch with their hind claws

Aggressive bucks may spray urine

All teeth continue to grow throughout the rabbit's lifetime

Rabbit neutrophils have prominent eosinophilic granules

Drugs contraindicated for use in rabbits include lincomycin, procaine, ampicillin, and erythromycin

FERRET
(Mustela putorius furo)
DATA CHART

Life span	6–12 years
Varieties	Fitch or sable (buff with black guard hairs, black mask, and black points on feet, body, and tail); recessive coat colors include the albino (English), Siamese (brown guard hairs and points), Silver mitt (sable with white feet and chest patch), and Siamese-silver mitt
Normal body temperature	100.8°–104°F (38°–40°C)
Respiration	33–36 breaths per minute
Pulse	250 per minute (avg.)
Weight	Males (hobs): 1–2.7 kg (2–6 lb) Females (jills): 0.45–0.9 kg (1–3 lb)
Blood collection sites	Caudal vein, jugular vein
Diet	Moist and dry dog, cat, or mink food; commercial ferret food Occasional low fiber tablescraps
Common diseases	Hyperestrogenism (jills), canine distemper, human influenza, urinary calculi, insulinomas, ear mites, fleas, abscesses
Breeding information	
• **Puberty**	9–12 months
• **Age to neuter**	6–8 months
• **Breeding season**	March–August (jills); December–July (hobs)
• **Gestation**	39–46 days (42 avg.)
• **Litter size**	2–17 (8 avg.)

• **Signs of estrus**	Swelling of the vulva NOTE: Jills that are not going to be bred should be neutered to prevent a potentially fatal hyperestrogenism-induced bone marrow hypoplasia
Neonates	Fuzzy hair at 2 days, teeth erupt at 14 days, eyes and ears open at 28–37 days Wean at 6–8 weeks (300–450 g) Reach adult weight at 16 weeks
Sex determination	Hobs are larger than jills and have an os penis; testes descend only during the breeding season
Miscellaneous	Both sexes have a musk-producing anal gland Ferrets can be trained to use a litter box

Bibliography

Ackerman L: *Biology, Husbandry, and Health Care of Reptiles: Parts I–III.* Neptune, NJ, TFH Publications, 1997.

Anderson LC: Guinea pig husbandry and medicine. *Vet Clin North Am Small Anim Pract* 17(5):1045–1060, 1987.

Besch-Williford CL: Biology and medicine of the ferret. *Vet Clin North Am Small Anim Pract* 17(5):1155–1183, 1987.

Exotic Animals: A Veterinary Handbook. Trenton, NJ, Veterinary Learning Systems, 1995.

Fox JG (ed): *Biology and Diseases of the Ferret.* Philadelphia, Lea & Febiger, 1988.

Frye FL: *Biomedical and Surgical Aspects of Captive Reptile Husbandry.* Malabar, Krieger Publishing, 1991.

Harkness JE: Rabbit husbandry and medicine. *Vet Clin North Am Small Anim Pract* 17(5):1019–1044, 1987.

Harkness JE, Wagner JE: *The Biology and Medicine of Rabbits and Rodents*, ed 4. Philadelphia, Williams & Wilkins, 1995.

Jacobson ER: Reptiles. *Vet Clin North Am Small Anim Pract* 17(5):1203–1225, 1987.

Ostrow M: *Goldfish.* New York, Barron's Publishing, 1985.

Reeves D: *Guidelines for the Care and Management of Miniature Pet Pigs.* Santa Barbara, CA, Veterinary Practice Publishing, 1991.

Ryland LM, Bernard SL, Gorham JR: A clinical guide to the pet ferret. *Compend Contin Educ Pract Vet* 5(1):25–32, 1983.

Stoskopf MK (ed): Tropical fish medicine. *Vet Clin North Am Small Anim Pract* 18(2):283–474, 1988.

Wagner JE, Farrar PL: Husbandry and medicine of small rodents. *Vet Clin North Am Small Anim Pract* 17(5):1061–1081, 1987.

NOTES